Contents

Introduction

This book is a tool to give your students practice in taking standardized tests. Research shows that students who are acquainted with the scoring format of standardized tests score higher on those tests. The concepts presented in this book are typically found on standardized tests in Reading and Language Arts for this grade level. The goal of this book is to improve students' ability to perform well on standardized tests. Students will have multiple opportunities to practice answering items in multiple-choice format, as well as to respond to open-ended items and writing prompts.

The tracking progress charts can help you pinpoint areas of weakness and strength with particular skills.

The book is divided into two main sections. The first section includes Test Tips and Practice for four main areas: Reading, Language Arts, Vocabulary, and Writing. Test Tips provide a review of common skills and terms as well as strategies related to the topic. The Reading section focuses on literary texts (stories, poems, and drama) and informational texts (nonfiction and technical). The Language Arts section covers grammar, usage, and mechanics, as well as editing and revising skills. The Vocabulary section covers skills related to vocabulary acquisition, such as using context clues to determine the meaning of unfamiliar words and analyzing word relationships. The Writing section focuses on three types of writing prompts: opinion, informative, and narrative. The second section provides Practice Tests for each area. For an authentic testing experience, students will record their answers to test items on an answer sheet.

Tracking Progress Chart

Objective	Practice Item	Test Item	Mastery Yes	Mastery No	Comments
Literary Texts					
Understand and analyze plot. * (RL.3.3)	**4, 19, 21**	**2, 18**			
Understand and analyze characters.* (RL.3.3)	**2, 6, 13, 25**	**4, 20, 33**			
Understand and analyze setting.	**11, 18**	**12, 23**			
Understand and analyze theme.* (RL.3.2)	**16**	**14, 24, 26**			
Understand and analyze point of view. * (RL.3.6)	**24**	**3, 28**			
Understand and analyze elements of poetry.	**22, 29**	**25, 32**			
Understand and analyze elements of drama.	**14, 15**	**16, 17**			
Make inferences from literary text.	**5, 8, 9**	**5, 9, 11, 22**			
Analyze and understand elements and structures of literary texts.	**3**	**19**			
Identify specific details and events in a literary text.* (RL.3.1)	**7, 20, 27, 30**	**8, 27, 29**			
Analyze how illustrations contribute to the meaning of a literary text.* (RL.3.7)	**23**	**13**			
Identify and understand figurative use of language in literary texts.* (RL.3.4)	**1, 17, 28**	**10, 15, 31**			
Identify the main idea of a text and the details that support it.* (RL.3.2)	**10, 26, 32, 33**	**1, 7, 30**			
Summarize literary texts. * (RL.3.2)	**12, 31**	**6, 21**			

*Aligns to Common Core State Standard

Objective	Practice Item	Test Item	Mastery Yes	Mastery No	Comments
Informational Texts					
Identify the main idea of a text and the details that support it.* (RI.3.2)	**1, 8, 10**	**34, 43**			
Analyze an author's perspective, argument, and point of view.* (RI.3.6)	**15, 17, 18, 24**	**36, 37**			
Analyze how text structures of informational texts contribute to the development of ideas.* (RI.3.5)	**13, 16**	**39, 51**			
Make inferences from an informational text.	**4, 9, 20, 23**	**42, 56, 60**			
Analyze and understand elements and features of informational texts.* (RI.3.5)	**3, 5, 26**	**48, 49**			
Summarize informational texts.* (RI.3.2)	**27**	**50, 58**			
Identify specific details, facts, or events in a text.* (RI.3.1)	**6, 7, 12, 14, 21, 28**	**35, 40, 45, 53, 54, 55, 59**			
Analyze how media and graphics contribute to a topic or issue.* (RI.3.7)	**22**	**44**			
Identify and understand academic, domain-specific, and technical words in informational texts.* (RI.3.4)	**2, 11**	**38, 41, 47, 57**			
Evaluate arguments and claims and how they are supported by evidence.	**19, 25**	**46, 52**			

Objective	Practice Item	Test Item	Mastery Yes	Mastery No	Comments
Language Conventions					
Demonstrate control of grammar, usage, and sentence structure.* (L.3.1)	**7, 20**	**5, 18**			
Identify parts of speech, such as nouns, pronouns, verbs, adjectives, and adverbs.* (L.3.1a)	**1, 8**	**1, 16**			
Use regular and irregular plural nouns correctly.* (L.3.1b)	**3**	**2, 24**			
Use regular and irregular verbs correctly.* (L.3.1d)	**4**	**4, 17**			
Use comparative and superlative adjectives and adverbs correctly.* (L.3.1g)	**5, 16, 17**	**14**			
Use simple, compound, and complex sentences correctly.* (L.3.1i)	**9**	**13, 20**			
Use prepositional phrases correctly.	**2**	**3, 7**			
Use verb tense correctly.* (L.3.1e)	**6, 13**	**6, 8**			
Understand agreement.* (L.3.1f)	**12**	**11**			
Use possessives correctly.* (L.3.2d)	**11**	**15, 19**			
Use pronouns correctly.	**10, 14**	**9**			
Use frequently confused words correctly.	**15**	**10**			
Avoid common usage problems.	**18, 19**	**12, 34**			
Demonstrate control of standard English conventions and mechanics.* (L.3.2)	**24, 36, 39, 40**	**29, 32, 39**			
Use capitalization correctly, including capitalizing titles.*(L.3.2a)	**21, 26, 34, 35**	**21, 23, 30, 35**			
Use punctuation correctly.* (L.3.2)	**23, 29, 31**	**26, 28, 36, 40**			
Use commas correctly.* (L.3.2b, L.3.2c)	**22, 27, 37**	**22, 33**			
Use quotation marks correctly.* (L.3.2c)	**25, 28, 38**	**31, 37**			
Use correct spelling.* (L.3.2e, L.3.2f)	**30, 32, 33**	**25, 27, 38**			

Objective	Practice Item	Test Item	Mastery Yes	Mastery No	Comments
Vocabulary					
Identify synonyms and antonyms.	**3, 11, 14**	**42, 49**			
Use context clues in sentences and paragraphs to decode new vocabulary.* (L.3.4a)	**1, 13**	**43, 50**			
Identify and understand figurative use of language.* (L.3.5a)	**5**	**44**			
Identify and use correctly multiple-meaning words.* (L.3.4)	**6**	**47**			
Distinguish shades of meaning among closely related words.* (L.3.5c)	**8, 15**	**48**			
Categorize words based on real-life connections between words and their use.* (L.3.5b)	**9**	**46**			
Identify and use suffixes, prefixes, and roots to understand and create words.* (L.3.4b)	**4, 12**	**41, 52**			
Understand word relationships.* (L.3.5)	**10**	**51**			
Understand how to use dictionary entries to determine pronunciation and clarify meaning.* (L.3.4d)	**2, 7**	**45**			
Writing					
Write opinion essays.* (W.3.1)	**Prompt 1**	**Prompt 1**			
Write informative essays.* (W.3.2)	**Prompt 2**	**Prompt 2**			
Write narrative essays.* (W.3.3)	**Prompt 3**	**Prompt 3**			

Reading
Test Tips and Practice

Name ______________________________ Date ______________

Taking Reading Tests

In the Reading Test Tips and Practice section, you will read some tips for answering multiple-choice questions and open-ended questions. Next, you will review common skills and terms and learn about strategies for answering different kinds of questions. Then, you will be asked to read stories and passages and answer questions.

Answering Multiple-Choice Questions

Here are some tips for taking any reading test:

- First, **read the passage as if you were not taking a test.** Do this to get an idea of the topic of the passage. Keep reading even if you do not understand the passage at first.
- Next, **think about the big picture.** To do this, ask yourself the following questions as you read:
  - What is the title?
  - What do you think is the main idea of a nonfiction passage, or what is the theme of a fiction passage?
  - Why did the author write the passage? To inform? To entertain? To show how to do something?
- Then, **read the questions.** This will help you know what information to look for when you read the passage a second time.
- Read the passage again. **Underline information** that helps you answer the questions. This will help you when filling in the answers.
- **Go back to the questions.** Try to answer each one in your mind before looking at the answer choices.
- Finally, **read *all* the answer choices and get rid of those that are not correct.** After this, mark the best answer. Remember, one answer is best. Some answer choices are not correct. Some are about the wrong part of the story. Some include too much information. Some include too little information.

Name ______________________ Date ______________

Answering Open-Ended Questions

Reading tests often include open-ended questions. These may be short-answer or extended-response questions. These kinds of questions do not have answer choices. You will write your answer.

Here are some tips for answering open-ended questions:

- Read the whole story or passage. Pay close attention to the most important events and characters. Make notes about the most important information.
- Read each question carefully. If you cannot answer the question at first, skip it and come back to it later.
- Return to the passage and skim it over. Look for details or examples you need to write your answer.
- When you write your answer, use details from the passage. Be sure to use correct spelling, grammar, and punctuation.

Scoring of Open-Ended Reading Questions:

Score of 3: You have written the correct answer and included details or examples from the text.

Score of 2: You have written only part of the answer. You have included at least one detail from the text. Your answer has some errors.

Score of 1: **Your answer is not complete.** Either you did not understand or you did not include details from the text. The details you included are not complete or are wrong. Your answer has some errors.

Score of 0: Your answer has too little information to be scored or is incorrect in many ways. Here are some reasons a response might get a score of zero.

- Answer is blank or too short to be scored.
- Answer is off-topic.
- Answer is written in a language other than English.
- Your handwriting cannot be read.

Name ______________________ Date ______________

Tips for Reading Literature

Summarizing

Follow these steps to choose the best answer to a **summary** question:

Step 1: Read the story or passage slowly and carefully. Look for the main characters, the problem, and the most important details.

Step 2: Think about each answer choice. Get rid of those that tell a single detail. Get rid of the ones that have little or nothing to do with the passage. Look for the most important details.

Step 3: Choose the answer that covers the important ideas in the whole passage. Make sure it tells about the main characters, the problem, and the most important details.

Making Inferences

Sometimes there is an idea in a passage that the author is trying to say but does not state directly. Think about both what the author says and what you know. Put the author's ideas and your ideas together to make an **inference**. Follow these steps to answer inference questions:

Step 1: Quickly read the story one time. Then carefully read it again. Think about the test question as your read.

Step 2: Find key words in the answer choices that match words in the story.

Step 3: Think about what the author said and what you know. This will help you find the correct answer.

Understanding Main Ideas and Supporting Details

The most important point in a paragraph or story is the **main idea**. Follow these steps to identify a main idea:

Step 1: Read the story and identify the topic.

Step 2: Look at the details. How are the details all alike? The details should all tell about the main idea. **Hint:** Pay attention to the first and last sentences. You may find a sentence that tells the main idea.

Step 3: State the main idea in your own words. Then, look for an answer choice that closely matches your own. Be careful not to choose an answer that tells just one detail.

Step 4: Check to make sure that the passage details all tell about the main idea you chose.

Name ______________________ Date ______________

Analyzing Character

A **character** is a person or animal in a story, poem, or play. An author tells about a character in six different ways:

- by describing how the character looks and dresses
- by letting the reader hear the character speak
- by showing the reader how the character acts
- by letting the reader know the character's thoughts and feelings
- by showing what other characters think or say about the character
- by telling the reader what the character is like (such as *kind*, *mean*, *brave*, and so on)

Identifying Setting

Setting is the time and place of a story, poem, or play. The setting can affect the events of the plot. To identify the setting, look for clues that answer the questions *Where did this happen?* and *When did this happen?*

Analyzing Plot

Plot is the series of events that makes up a story. The plot tells what happens. Most plots are told in the order the events happened.

- Many times a story begins with an introduction that tells who the characters are and what their problem is.
- Look for time-order words like *first*, *next*, *then*, and *finally* to help you tell the order of events.
- The final part of the story is where the characters' problems are solved and the story ends.

Identifying Point of View

Point of view is who is telling a story. Point of view can be first person or third person.

- First-person point of view: One of the characters, using the pronoun *I*, tells the story.
- Third-person point of view: A narrator knows everything and tells all about the characters and their problems.

Name ______________________________ Date ________________

Analyzing Theme

The **theme** of a story is the main idea, or lesson, that the author is trying to teach. A theme may or may not be told in the story. You will have to figure it out by thinking about the characters and events. Follow these steps to identify the theme:

Step 1: Think about the main problem of the story and how the characters act.

Step 2: Ask yourself if the characters learned any lessons.

Step 3: Choose the answer that best tells the lesson the characters learned.

Analyzing Elements of Poetry

Rhyme – words that have the same ending sound

Example: sweet and treat, care and their

Rhythm – repeating sounds or beats in phrases or sentences

Identifying Literary Devices

Authors use different literary devices to help readers form pictures in their minds. Test questions may ask you to find literary devices or to tell what they mean.

Alliteration – repeating of the same beginning consonant sounds in words that are close together

Example: Sally sells seashells by the seashore.

Figurative language – describes one thing by comparing it to a different thing

Examples: Maria sings like a bird.
That baby is cute as a button.

Imagery – words and phrases that describe something using the five senses: sight, touch, smell, sound, or taste

Example: The red and yellow leaves fall to the ground. (sight) They crunch under my feet. (sound) I pick one up and it crumbles in my hand. (touch)

Speaker – The narrator in a poem is called the speaker.

Name ________________________________ Date ______________

Literature

Read the story. Then, answer the questions. On your answer sheet, darken the circle for each correct answer for multiple-choice items. For the short-answer item, write your answer on a separate sheet of paper.

How the Chipmunk Got Its Stripes:

A Native American Folktale

One evening, a very long time ago, a bear was out walking. This was back when animals could speak and before chipmunks had stripes down their backs.

"I can do anything, anything, anything," said Bear as he walked. "I can do anything, anything at all!"

"Really?" asked a little chipmunk.

"Yes," said Bear. "I am the strongest animal. I can do anything I want to do."

"Can you stop the sun from rising in the morning?" asked Chipmunk.

"Of course I can," Bear answered.

"Are you sure?" asked Chipmunk with a sly smile.

"I am very sure," said Bear.

It grew dark and stars began to appear in the night sky. Bear sat down facing east where the sun had risen that morning and every other morning as far back as he could remember.

Chipmunk snuggled down into his hole in the ground, laughing himself to sleep at how foolish Bear was.

But Bear did not sleep. He told the sun, "Do not rise in the morning." He said it over and over again all night.

Finally, after many hours, Chipmunk climbed out of his hole in the ground and sat down next to Bear. "The sun will rise," said Chipmunk.

"The sun will not rise," said Bear, but there was already a golden glow in the east. "Do not rise!" he ordered the sun, but the sun did not obey.

"Look!" Chipmunk shouted. "The sun is rising!"

This made Bear very angry. Quick as lightning, Bear shot out one big

Name ______________________ Date ______________

paw and pinned Chipmunk to the ground. "Perhaps I cannot stop the sun from rising," said Bear, "but I can stop you."

Chipmunk realized he was in big trouble now. "Oh, Bear," he said, "I was just kidding. Please let me go."

But Bear did not remove his paw. His claws pressed into Chipmunk's back.

"Look!" Chipmunk yelled. "The sun changed its mind. It's going back down."

Bear turned to see if he'd won after all, but the sun was exactly where it always was at that time of morning.

Chipmunk had tricked Bear into looking away. Bear's paw moved a little, too. It was just enough for Chipmunk to squirm free. But the tips of Bear's claws scraped painfully all the way down Chipmunk's back.

Chipmunk ran as fast as he could back to the safety of his hole in the ground. Eventually, Chipmunk's back healed, but there were still three long scars where Bear's claws had scratched him. This is how Chipmunk got his stripes.

Now, all chipmunks have stripes down their backs. Maybe the stripes are there as a reminder of what can happen when one animal teases another.

Name ______________________________ Date ____________________

1. Read the following sentence from the story.

Quick as lightning, Bear shot out one big paw and pinned Chipmunk to the ground.

What does quick as lightning tell you about Bear?

A Bear is very big.

B Bear is very mean.

C Bear is very smart.

D Bear is very fast.

2. How will Chipmunk **most likely** act toward Bear in the future?

A He will become Bear's best friend.

B He will stay away from Bear.

C He will try to beat Bear in a fight.

D He will play another joke on Bear.

3. How can you tell that this story is a folktale?

A It is a true story.

B It has words that rhyme.

C It has animals that talk.

D It tells events from the author's life.

4. What happened **just before** Bear trapped Chipmunk with his paw?

A Chipmunk shouted that the sun was rising.

B Bear repeatedly told the sun to not rise.

C Chipmunk tricked Bear into looking away.

D Chipmunk ran back to the safety of his hole.

5. Chipmunk laughed himself to sleep because

A he knew that nothing could stop the sun from rising.

B he had never heard an animal talk before.

C he couldn't believe he got stripes on his back.

D he realized he had made Bear very angry.

6. Why do you think Bear believes he can stop the sun from rising?

Name ______________________________ Date ______________

Read the story. Then, answer the questions. On your answer sheet, darken the circle for each correct answer for multiple-choice items. For the short-answer item, write your answer on a separate sheet of paper.

Paul in the Woods

Paul and his friends went to explore the woods near Paul's house. As they walked down a path, Paul noticed a large blackberry bush. He decided to pick some berries for a snack.

Just as Paul reached in to pick some berries, he heard a soft "Coo-coo-coo." He listened carefully and started to look around to see if he could find where the sound was coming from. Suddenly a gray bird fell to the ground. It flopped about. Paul thought that the bird had a broken wing so he stooped to pick it up. But the bird flopped just ahead of him. So Paul followed the bird. When they were far away from the bush, it flew up high in a pine tree.

Paul went back to the blackberry bush. He saw two beautiful white eggs in a nest no higher than his head. He didn't touch the eggs, and Paul and his friends decided to look for another blackberry bush.

Later they saw the bird fly back to her nest. They could hear her saying "Coo-coo-coo," as though she were glad her nest had not been disturbed.

7. Paul reached into the bush because he

A saw a bird's nest.

B wanted to pick blackberries.

C heard a strange sound.

D wanted to help the bird.

8. From the story, you can guess that the mother bird

A was worried about her eggs.

B didn't want Paul to pick berries.

C had a broken wing.

D wanted to build another nest.

Name ________________________________ Date ________________

9. The mother bird **most likely**

A wanted the berries for herself.

B pretended that her wing was broken.

C had been sitting there a long time.

D could not fly very far.

10. Which of these is another good name for this story?

A Paul Picks Fruit

B Let's Go Exploring

C How to Pick Berries

D A Clever Bird

11. Which of these are part of the setting of this story?

A eggs and snack food

B a boy and his friends

C bushes and pine trees

D a kind boy and a smart bird

12. What is the **best** summary of the story?

A A bird flopped on the ground. Paul tried to help the bird, but it said, "Coo-coo-coo." This made Paul decide to go looking for a snack somewhere else.

B Paul saw a nest when he went to pick some blackberries. Soon he found the mother bird, but she scared Paul. The bird wouldn't let Paul touch the eggs in the nest. Paul and his friends went off to explore the woods.

C Paul was picking blackberries when a bird fell out of the bush and flopped around. When Paul reached for the bird, it flew. Then, Paul saw a bird's nest in the bush. He left it alone and the bird came back to its nest.

D Paul and his friends went blackberry picking. They found a bird's nest. The bird sang "Coo-coo-coo." Paul and his friends went in search of a different bush.

13. What two details in the story show that Paul is kind?

Name ______________________________ Date ______________

Read the play. Then, answer the questions. On your answer sheet, darken the circle for each correct answer for multiple-choice items. For the short-answer item, write your answer on a separate sheet of paper.

Attack of the Dust Bunnies

Cast

Narrator
Mom
Robert, an 8-year-old boy
Val, his 6-year-old sister

Narrator: It is 3 o'clock on a Saturday afternoon, and Grandma is coming to visit.

Mom: Robert, did you clean your room yet?

Robert: M-o-m! I am right in the middle of my computer game. Can't I do it later?

Mom: Later will be too late. Grandma will be here in two hours, and she will be staying in your room.

Robert: Does that mean I get to sleep in the living room in my sleeping bag?

Mom: Yes. Now please help me get ready for Grandma. Clean your room!

Val: I'll help you, Robert.

Robert: You can't help. You're too little.

Val: That's what you think! *(She points to her spotless room.)* Not a dust bunny in sight!

Robert: Hmmmm … maybe. *(He looks around, runs a finger across the chest, and inspects it for dust.)* Not a speck of dust here. All right, you can help.

Val: Okay! Now get ready to attack the dust bunnies! *(She shoves a broom under Robert's bed and sweeps out a baseball cap covered with dust.)* Look at this dusty cap I found! It almost got eaten by dust bunnies!

Robert: Hey! I've been looking for that cap for a long time. I guess it did get covered by dust balls. *(He brushes the dust off his cap.)*

Narrator: An hour later, not a speck of dust was in sight.

Mom: Wow, this room looks great! And you found your favorite cap!

Name ______________________________ Date ______________

Robert:	Val found it. For a little sister, she's not too bad. *(He grins.)*
Mom:	I like it when the two of you help each other out. That's how families work together.
Narrator:	When it is time for bed, Robert sets up his tent in the living room. He invites Val to "camp out" in it, too.
Robert:	Hey, Val?
Val:	What?
Robert:	Thanks for all the help today.
Val:	It was easy! *(She grins, happy with the praise.)* Except there's one more dust bunny I haven't attacked yet.
Robert:	Where? *(Robert looks around the tent.)*
Val:	Right here! *(She smacks Robert with her pillow. They both laugh.)*
Robert:	M-o-m!

14. "Attack of the Dust Bunnies" is a play because

A it tells a funny story.

B it has rhythm and rhyme.

C it has a cast and dialogue.

D it tells how to do something.

15. How many people are needed to perform this play?

A 2

B 4

C 6

D 8

16. The lesson of this play is

A rooms should be clean.

B camping out is fun.

C grandmothers love their grandkids.

D families work together.

Name ______________________________ Date ______________

17. Read the sentences from the play.

> Look at this dusty cap I found! It almost got eaten by the dust bunnies!

What does eaten by the dust bunnies mean in the sentence?

A The cap was covered in dust.

B Rabbits were eating the cap.

C The cap had dusty rabbits on it.

D Dusty rabbits were wearing caps.

18. What is the setting of the play?

A a campground

B inside Robert's tent

C Robert and Val's house

D Robert's grandmother's house

19. What is Robert's problem at the beginning of the play?

A Robert must clean his room, but he'd rather finish his game.

B Val wants to help, but she is too little to work.

C Grandma has arrived for a visit and doesn't have a place to sleep.

D Robert wants to go camping, but his Grandma is coming to visit.

20. Val helps by

A showing how clean her room is.

B brushing dust off caps.

C inspecting the room for dust.

D sweeping under the bed.

21. Complete the chart to show the order of events in the play.

Mom asks Robert to clean his room.

Mom tells Robert and Val they did a good job.

Robert and Val have fun getting ready to "camp out" in the living room.

Name ______________________ Date ______________

Read the poem. Then, answer the questions. On your answer sheet, darken the circle for each correct answer for multiple-choice items. For the short-answer item, write your answer on a separate sheet of paper.

Our Tree House

by R.M. Callahan

The big oak tree stood in our yard
Like our father watching us play.
Father gazed up at its strong branches
Reaching to the sky.
What could they hold?
"A tree house," he said.
He climbed into the branches
And tied pieces in place with rope.
"The tree would be sad
If we used nails," he said.
First floor, then walls, and then
A house against the blue sky!
Then he unrolled a rope ladder
And climbed back down.
My sister and I sat at his feet.
He said we could use the tree house
Only when he or Mother was home.
We could not fight.
We had to treat the tree with respect.
We promised all these things.
Then we climbed the rope ladder
Up into the branches.
We looked down and saw a boy and girl.
It felt like looking in a mirror.
Father asked their parents
If they could play.
Now we all climb the rope ladder
Into the branches together.
We can see the whole neighborhood
And sometimes,
When the sky sparkles blue,
We can see the whole world!

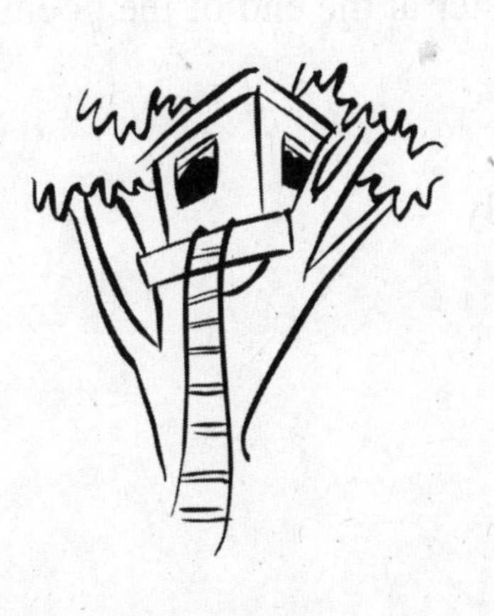

Name ______________________ Date ______________

22. The poet compares the oak tree to

A a tree house.

B his father.

C a grandfather.

D a tower.

23. Look at the picture on page 15. Where does this poem take place?

A in a bedroom

B in the sky

C in a tree

D underground

24. The reader can tell that the speaker of the poem is a

A father.

B bird.

C child.

D builder.

25. Which word **best** describes the speaker and his sister at the end of the poem?

A silly

B friendly

C angry

D tired

26. What is the main idea of "Our Tree House"?

Name ______________________ Date ______________

Read the poem. Then, answer the questions. On your answer sheet, darken the circle for each correct answer for multiple-choice items. For the short-answer items, write your answers on a separate sheet of paper.

Sunflowers in the Rain

Sunflowers standing in the rain
heads bent tightly together.
They never, never complain
about the drenching weather.

Soon the sun will shine and dry
their pretty sunflower faces.
Then they'll hold their heads up high
and shake off all rain's traces.

27. How do the sunflowers look when it is raining?

A They are straight and tall.

B They are bent over.

C They are pretty.

D They face the sun.

28. Read these lines from the poem.

> Sunflower standing in the rain
> heads bent tightly together.

What part of the sunflowers are the head?

A leaves

B stems

C roots

D flowers

Name ______________________________ Date ______________

29. Read the lines from the poem.

> Soon the sun will shine and <u>dry</u>
> Their pretty sunflower faces.
> Then they'll hold their heads up <u>high</u>

The underlined words are examples of

A rhyme.

B mood.

C symbols.

D stanzas.

30. How does the author help the reader understand sunflowers?

A by comparing sunflowers to weather

B by explaining what sunflowers do in the rain

C by showing the steps in a sunflower's growth

D by telling a funny story about a flowerbed

31. Which statement is the **best** summary of the poem?

A Sunflowers are outside in the rain and sunshine.

B Sunflowers are pretty and never complain.

C Sunflowers bend over in the rain and then stand up to face the sun.

D Sunflowers stand, bend over, hold their heads up, and shake.

32. What is the main idea of "Sunflowers in the Rain"?

33. What is one detail from the poem that supports the main idea?

Name ________________________________ Date ____________________

Tips for Reading Informational Texts

Identifying the Main Idea and Supporting Details

The most important point in a passage is the **main idea.** The main idea must be about the entire passage, not just a part of it. Follow these steps to find the main idea.

Step 1: Read the passage. Decide what the topic is. The title and headings are clues to the passage's topic.

Step 2: Look at what all the details have in common. The details should point to the main idea. **Hint:** Pay attention to the first and last sentences. You may find a sentence that states the main idea.

Step 3: State the main idea in your own words. Then, look for an answer that matches your own. Be careful not to choose a detail that just supports the main idea as your answer.

Step 4: Check to make sure that the details in the passage support your answer.

Identifying Author's Purpose

There are four general purposes authors have for writing. They are **to inform, to persuade, to express,** and **to entertain**.

Use the steps below for help in answering questions about purpose:

Step 1: Look in the text for clues such as the ones below.

- illustrations, diagrams, maps, charts, headings, and numbered items **(to inform)**
- words like *should* and *must*, or *worst* and *best* **(to persuade)**
- use of the word *I* and words about feelings **(to express)**
- use of make-believe, dialogue, rhymes, adventure, or humor **(to entertain)**

Step 2: Look for the choice that most closely matches the clues.

Name ______________________ Date ______________

Analyzing Text Structure

Understanding the way a text is organized can help readers follow the writer's ideas. Four types of organization are listed below.

- **Cause and effect** tells what happened and why it happened. It may have clue words and phrases that signal cause and effect such as *because*, *since*, and *so that.*
- **Time order** shows events in the order they happened. Look for time-order words, such as *first*, *next*, *then*, and *finally.*
- **Compare and contrast** tells how things are alike and different. Some clue words that tell how things are different are *but*, *either*, *or*, *different*, and *yet*. Some clue words that tell how things are alike are *also*, *alike*, *as well*, *both*, and *too.*
- **Problem and solution** presents a problem and then tells a solution for the problem.

Use the steps below to help analyze text structure:

Step 1: Look for clue words that tell about a kind of organization.

Step 2: Look for important ideas. See whether these ideas are connected.

Step 3: Look for the answer choice that best matches the organization.

Using Text Features

Here are some examples of **text features:**

headings	**captions**	**labels**	**maps**
charts	**tables**	**diagrams**	**illustrations**

Text features such as headings, captions, and labels help readers find information.

Text features such as maps, charts, tables, diagrams, and illustrations present information in picture form.

When you see text features, use the steps below:

Step 1: Read the title, labels, and legend.

Step 2: Read numbers and other information carefully.

Step 3: Look for clues in the text feature that connect information to the text.

Name ______________________ Date ______________

Identifying Point of View

The **point of view** is how the author feels about a subject. Follow these steps to answer questions about the author's point of view:

Step 1: Look for words that tell how the author feels about the subject. See if the author is for or against something.

Step 2: Answer the question in your own words.

Step 3: Look for the choice that best matches your own answer.

Summarizing a Text

Follow these steps to choose the best answer to a **summary** question:

Step 1: Look for the main idea and the **most important** supporting details as you read the passage slowly and carefully.

Step 2: Think about each answer choice. Get rid of those that tell a single detail from the passage. Get rid of those that tell a general statement about the passage but tell no important details. Get rid of those that have little or nothing to do with the passage.

Step 3: Choose the answer that is about the whole passage. Make sure it includes the main idea and only the important supporting details.

Making Inferences

Sometimes there is an idea in a passage that the author does not state directly. An author may tell something about the idea, but you must also think about what you know about it. Put the author's ideas and your ideas together to make an **inference**. Follow these steps to answer inference questions:

Step 1: Skim the passage one time. Then, carefully read it again.

Step 2: Find key words in the answer choices that match words in the passage.

Step 3: Think about what the author said and what you know. This will help you find the correct answer.

Name ______________________________ Date ______________

Informational Texts

Read the passage. Then, answer the questions. On your answer sheet, darken the circle for each correct answer for multiple-choice items. For the short-answer items, write your answers on a separate sheet of paper.

Komodo Dragons

Dragons are scary monsters in stories, legends, and movies. But have you ever wondered if they were real?

Are Dragons Real?

In 1912, a group of fishermen who went to Komodo Island had a scary experience. When they got near the island, they saw creatures that looked like dragons. The creatures were as big as the men's fishing boat. When they returned home, the men told their dragon stories. The stories did not get a lot of attention until fourteen years later.

In 1926, the American Museum of Natural History sponsored a trip back to Komodo. The scientists confirmed that the fishermen's stories were true. They studied the creatures and even brought two of them back alive. The creatures were called Komodo dragons.

Komodo dragons are monitor lizards.

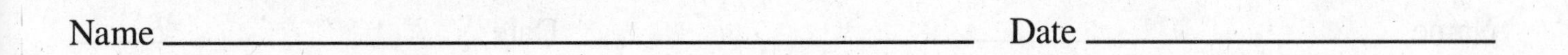
Name ______________________ Date ______________

What Do Komodo Dragons Look Like?

A Komodo dragon is the largest living lizard. The males and females look alike, except that the males are larger. Grown male lizards are about 9 feet long and weigh about 300 pounds. Female lizards are about 7 to 8 feet long and weigh about 150 pounds.

A Komodo dragon has a lizard-like head and a long neck. It has a long, forked tongue. It also has sharp teeth for hunting and eating.

A Komodo dragon is a fast runner. Its legs are short and strong. It also has a very strong sense of smell and can smell food from several miles away.

What Do Komodo Dragons Eat?

Komodo dragons eat meat. They hunt eggs, small deer, and wild pigs. They hide in the grass and wait. Then they lean out and bite the animal. A Komodo dragon can bring down a water buffalo. It also eats the meat of dead animals. Although Komodo dragons are not known to hunt humans, they have killed a few people.

Where Do Komodo Dragons Live?

In the wild, Komodo dragons live on four islands in the country of Indonesia. They dig small caves. They spend their days in these caves or in the shade under bushes.

Komodo dragons also live in zoos. The National Zoo in Washington, D.C., has a pair. These two dragons have hatched more dragons. Now you can see Komodo dragons in many zoos in the United States.

Name ________________________________ Date ________________

1. Which question is answered in the second paragraph?

   A What did the fishermen see on Komodo Island?

   B Where on Komodo Island did the fishermen go?

   C Who did the fishermen tell about what they saw?

   D Where can you see Komodo dragons today?

2. Read this sentence from the passage.

These two dragons have <u>hatched</u> more dragons.

   What does the word <u>hatch</u> mean?

   A see with the eyes

   B come out of an egg

   C close or fasten

   D chase in a circle

3. Under which heading will you find information about how a Komodo dragon moves around?

   A Are Dragons Real?

   B What Do Komodo Dragons Look Like?

   C What Do Komodo Dragons Eat?

   D Where Do Komodo Dragons Live?

4. Based on the passage, the author would **most likely** agree with the idea that

   A Komodo Island is a great place to go fishing.

   B Komodo dragons would make great pets.

   C Komodo dragons are rare animals.

   D Komodo dragons are only seen in movies.

5. What can you learn from the caption?

   A how Komodo dragons hunt

   B what Komodo dragons look like

   C where Komodo dragons live

   D what kind of lizard a Komodo dragon is

6. According to the passage, what event confirmed that "dragons" really existed?

7. What kind of food do Komodo dragons eat?

Name ______________________________ Date ______________

Read the passage. Then, answer the questions. On your answer sheet, darken the circle for each correct answer for multiple-choice items. For the short-answer item, write your answer on a separate sheet of paper.

Banana Plants

Banana plants are not planted from seeds. New plants grow from small shoots that sprout from the side of the mature plants. The new plants grow rapidly. They reach their full height in one year. The blossoms appear when the plants are about nine months old. Each plant has one cluster of flowers from which one bunch of bananas will grow.

It takes about three or four months for the fruit to grow large enough to be cut. Bananas are always cut when they are green. If they are allowed to ripen on the plant, they lose their flavor, and the skin bursts open.

After a bunch of bananas is cut, the plant dies and is cut down. Then the new shoots grow up to take the place of the old plant, and the cycle begins again.

8. Another good title for this passage would be

A Visiting a Banana Plantation.

B The Life Cycle of Banana Plants.

C How to Eat a Banana.

D Bananas Are Delicious.

9. How many times can bananas be harvested from a banana plant?

A 1

B 5

C 10

D 15

Name ______________________________ Date ______________

10. From this passage, the reader learns that

A banana plants are always planted from seeds.

B the banana skin always bursts open.

C bananas are always cut when they are ripe.

D bananas are cut when they are green.

11. Read this sentence from the passage.

> New plants grow from small shoots that sprout from the side of the <u>mature</u> plants.

What does the word <u>mature</u> mean?

A short

B green

C grown

D ripe

12.

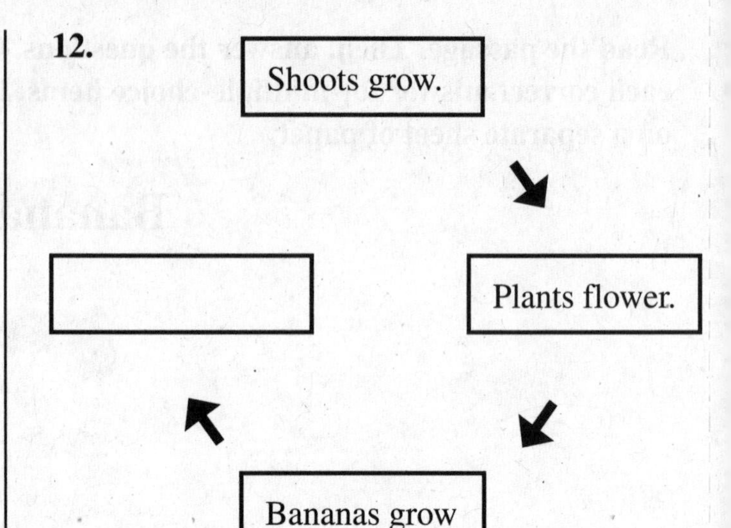

Which step completes the life cycle of a banana plant?

A Banana seeds are planted.

B The banana skin bursts open.

C New shoots grow from the old plant.

D Bananas are cut, and the plant dies.

13. How does the author tell the reader about a banana plant's life?

A by giving causes and effects

B by telling events in order

C by naming a problem and how it is solved

D by comparing with another plant

14. Why don't farmers allow bananas to ripen on the plant?

Name ______________________ Date ______________

Read the passage. Then, answer the questions. On your answer sheet, darken the circle for each correct answer for multiple-choice items. For the short-answer item, write your answer on a separate sheet of paper.

Dog Parks

Have you ever been to a dog park? These parks are built especially for dogs. Most dog parks have fences around them so that dogs can play without being on a leash. These fences keep dogs from running away or into the streets. Dogs enjoy the freedom of dog parks, and owners enjoy seeing their dogs have fun. Owners can toss a ball to their dogs or watch them play with other dogs.

Visiting a dog park is fun, but you should follow certain rules while you are there. These rules make parks safe and fun for dogs and people alike.

- Keep your dog under control. Your dog should be well trained. Even when it is playing, your dog should come when you call it.
- Pick up after your dog to keep the area clean.
- Do not play with strange dogs. Some dogs may not like strangers.
- If two dogs get into a fight, stay away. You could get bitten. Let adults take care of the problem. They can safely separate the dogs.

If you keep these rules in mind, you and your dog will have a great time at the dog park.

Name ____________________________ Date ______________

15. Which sentence **best** tells how the author feels about dog parks?

A Most dog parks have fences around them.

B Dog parks are not safe because dogs fight.

C Dogs are fun to play with.

D Dog parks are fun places if you follow the rules.

16. How is the information in this passage mainly organized?

A Reasons for going to a dog park are given.

B Rules for a dog park are listed.

C Dog parks are compared to other parks.

D Directions to a dog park are given.

17. The author's **main** purpose for this passage is

A to get people to go to dog parks.

B to compare different kinds of parks.

C to inform people about dog parks.

D to tell an interesting story.

18. Which sentence is the author's opinion about dog parks?

A These fences keep dogs from running away or into the streets.

B Visiting a dog park is fun, but you should follow certain rules while you are there.

C These parks are built especially for dogs.

D Owners can toss a ball to their dogs or watch them play with other dogs.

19. Which sentence supports the claim that you should not try to break up a dogfight?

A You could get bitten.

B Your dog should be well trained.

C These parks are built especially for dogs.

D Dogs enjoy the freedom of dog parks.

20. Why do most dog parks have fences around them?

A to keep dogs from biting strangers

B to keep other dogs away

C to keep dogs from making a mess

D to keep dogs safe from traffic

21. List three rules that you should follow when you go to a dog park.
Use information from "Dog Parks" in your answer.

Name ______________________________ Date ______________

Read the passage. Then, answer the questions. On your answer sheet, darken the circle for each correct answer for multiple-choice items. For the short-answer item, write your answer on a separate sheet of paper.

Pretzel-Stand Pretzels at Home

Have you ever eaten pretzels from a pretzel stand? They are not the little crunchy pretzels you buy at the grocery store. They are big, soft pretzels dotted with salt. They come wrapped in wax paper. They are warm, chewy, and delicious. Now you can make and enjoy them at home.

The first step is to get an adult to help you. It is not safe to cook without an adult. (Besides, you might want help in cleaning up!) Next, get the ingredients:

- Brown sugar
- Salt
- Yeast
- Water
- Flour
- Butter
- Baking soda
- One egg

You will also need measuring cups, measuring spoons, mixing bowls, a spoon to mix with, a cookie sheet, a large pot, a big slotted spoon, a fork, and a brush.

Start by measuring 4 tablespoons of brown sugar, 2 teaspoons of salt, 1 tablespoon of yeast, and 1 cup of warm water. Combine them in the mixing bowl. Then add 3-1/2 cups of flour. Mix until the dough is smooth. Cover the dough and put it in the refrigerator to rest overnight.

The next day, grease the cookie sheet with butter. Then shape the dough into six balls. Roll the balls into ropes. Bend each rope into a "U" shape. Then bring the ends of the "U" together and twist them once around each other.

Next, fold the twist over into the center of the "U." Press the ends into the dough at the bottom of the "U." Now, it looks like a pretzel! Put the pretzels on the cookie sheet, and let them sit for about half an hour. They will rise, getting a little bigger.

Mix 4 cups of water and 2 tablespoons of baking soda in the pot. Have your adult helper bring the water and soda to a boil. Next, have your helper drop the pretzels into the pot for 10 seconds each. Use the slotted spoon to take them out. Remember, only an adult should work with boiling water! Put the pretzels back on the cookie sheet.

Name ______________________ Date ______________

Crack the egg into a mixing bowl, and then add 1 teaspoon of water. Stir the egg and the water with the fork until they are mixed together well. Then brush the pretzels with the mixture and sprinkle them with coarse salt.

Have your adult helper heat the oven to 450 degrees. When the oven is hot, the pretzels can go in. Cook them 12–15 minutes, until they are golden brown. Your adult helper should take them out of the oven.

Let the pretzels cool a bit. Grab one while it is still warm and take a big, chewy bite. Delicious!

22. Why does the author include a two-column list in the passage?

A to show the ingredients for making pretzels

B to describe the steps for making pretzels

C to explain what tools you need to make pretzels

D to tell the history of the pretzel

23. Why does the author **most likely** say that only an adult should work with boiling water?

A Adults are taller.

B Adults enjoy it.

C A child could get burned.

D A child doesn't know when water is boiling.

24. Which sentence shows that the author likes pretzel-stand pretzels?

A They come wrapped in wax paper.

B They are warm, chewy, and delicious.

C Your adult helper should take them out of the oven.

D Let the pretzels cool a bit.

25. Which sentence supports the claim that you should only cook with an adult?

A Now you can make and enjoy this snack at home.

B Cover the dough and put it in the refrigerator to rest overnight.

C Have your adult helper heat the oven to 450 degrees.

D It is not safe to cook without an adult.

Name ______________________________ Date ______________

26. How is the information in the passage mainly organized?

A Steps on how to make pretzels are given.

B Pretzels are compared to other snack foods.

C The history of the pretzel is given.

D A story about making pretzels is told.

27. What is the best summary of the passage?

A Make pretzel-stand pretzels at home by following the directions step by step with an adult's help.

B Pretzel-stand pretzels are best eaten when they are still warm.

C Make pretzel dough by mixing together brown sugar, salt, yeast, water, and flour.

D To make dough into a pretzel shape, bend it into a "U" shape, twist the ends together, and fold the twist into the center.

28. Describe three important steps in the process of making pretzels.

Language Arts and Vocabulary

Test Tips and Practice

Name ______________________________ Date ______________

Taking Language Arts Tests

In the Language Arts Tips and Practice section, you will review common skills and terms about grammar, usage, and mechanics. Then, you will read passages that have errors and answer questions about how to fix the errors. You will also answer stand-alone questions.

Tips for Grammar and Usage

Identifying Nouns and Pronouns

A noun is a word used to name a person, place, thing, or idea.

> **Paula** went to the **library**. She checked out three **books** about **butterflies**.

A pronoun is a word used in place of one or more nouns or pronouns.

> I enjoy reading books. I like to read adventure stories with **my** sisters. **They** like **them** too.

Identifying Verbs

A verb is a word that shows action.

> Terry **swam** across the lake. Then, he **rested**. He **lay** down in the grass.

Identifying Adjectives and Adverbs

An adjective is a word used to describe a noun or a pronoun. Adjectives tell how something looks, tastes, feels, or sounds. Adjectives answer questions like *What kind? Which one? How many? How big?*

> Ms. Green bought **three green** apples, a **large** watermelon, and a pound of **sour** cherries.

An adverb is a word used to describe a verb. Adverbs answer questions like *Where? When? How?* Many adverbs end in *-ly*.

> When it rained, the children played **inside**. All games must be played **quietly**. They will play **outside tomorrow**.

Name ______________________ Date ______________

Using Correct Noun and Verb Agreement

When a noun names only one, use an action verb with *s.*

Margaret loves raisins.
The **bear sleeps** in a cave.
My **brother plays** the flute.

When a noun names only one, use the helping verb *is.*

Margaret is eating raisins.
The **bear is sleeping** in a cave.
My **brother is playing** the flute.

When a noun names more than one, the action verb does not have an *s.*

The **twins make** popcorn.
The three **puppies sit** in the window.
The **children walk** in the hall.

When a noun names more than one, use the helping verb *are.*

The **twins are making** popcorn.
The three **puppies are sitting** in the window.
The **children are walking** in the hall.

Using Correct Personal Pronouns

A pronoun refers to a noun or another pronoun. If a noun tells about only one, use the pronouns *he, him, she, her,* and *it*. If a noun tells about more than one, use the pronouns *we, us, they,* and *them*. If telling about yourself, use *I* and *me*.

I was playing with Mia. I hit a vase. **It** fell on the floor. Mia helped **me** clean **it** up. **She** is a good friend. After that, **we** went outside to play.

Name ______________________ Date ______________

Tips for Mechanics

Using Correct Capitalization

Capitalize the first word in every sentence.

Our school is having a big garage sale.

Capitalize the pronoun I.

My cousin and I had a puppet show.

Capitalize proper nouns.

A proper noun names a certain person, place, or thing.
Did you know that Coach Hales lived in England?

Capitalize the first, last, and important words in titles.

I was in the play "Goldilocks and the Three Bears."

Capitalize names of holidays.

We planted a tree on Arbor Day.

Using Correct Punctuation

End marks

Use a period at the end of a statement.

My neighbor drives a bus.

Use a question mark at the end of a question.

How do you get to Park Street?

Use an exclamation point at the end of an exclamation or command.

Wow! That's amazing!
Give me that, now!

Name ______________________ Date ______________

Commas
Use commas to separate items in a series.

We got pencils, pens, and crayons.

Use commas before *and*, *but*, *or*, *nor*, *for*, *so*, or *yet* when it joins the parts of a compound sentence.

I think bats are cool, but my brother is afraid of them.

Use commas in dates.

School is closed on Monday, May 27, 2013.

Use a comma after the opening of a friendly letter and after the closing of any letter.

Dear Mary,
Your friend,

Apostrophes
Use apostrophes in contractions.

can not .... can't
has not .... hasn't
will not............ won't

Use apostrophes to show who owns something.

a dog's collar
the boys' wallets
teacher's desk

Name ______________________ Date ______________

Language Arts

Read the passage. Then, answer the questions. On your answer sheet, darken the circle for each correct answer.

(1) People who live in cities often enjoy parks. **(2)** Recently, two families spent the entire day ______ our city park. **(3)** They beginned the morning with a canoe ride on the deep blue lake. **(4)** At noon, the families pulled out their ______ and had a picnic in the shade. **(5)** The park has a large playground. **(6)** Older children played on the large of the three slides.

1. Read sentence 1.

People who live in cities often enjoy parks.

What part of speech is the underlined word?

A noun **C** verb

B pronoun **D** adjective

2. Which word goes in the blank in sentence 2?

A down **C** during

B under **D** at

3. Which word goes in the blank in sentence 4?

A lunches's

B lunchs

C lunches

D lunchies

4. What is the correct way to write sentence 3?

A They begun the morning with a canoe ride on the deep blue lake.

B They began the morning with a canoe ride on the deep blue lake.

C They beginning the morning with a canoe ride on the deep blue lake.

D Correct as is.

5. What is the correct way to write sentence 6?

A Older children played on the largest of the three slides.

B Older children played on the larger of the three slides.

C Older children played on the more large of the three slides.

D Correct as is.

Name ________________________________ Date ______________

Read the passage. Then, answer the questions. On your answer sheet, darken the circle for each correct answer.

(1) Have you ever heard of a person who likes washing dishes? **(2)** My friend Dan will really enjoy it. **(3)** In fact, Dan washes dishes whenever he can. **(4)** Dan pulls a chair over to the sink, he can reach everything easily. **(5)** Dan likes the lemony smell of the liquid detergent. **(6)** He squeezes the bottle gently. **(7)** He watches the liquid soap stream into the water. **(8)** The soap mixes with the hot water. **(9)** Together, they create a mass of frothy white bubbles. **(10)** Dan makes Dan's work fun!

6. What is the correct way to write sentence 2?

A My friend Dan really enjoying it.

B My friend Dan really enjoys it.

C My friend Dan really enjoying it.

D Correct as is.

7. What is the correct way to write sentence 4?

A Dan pulls a chair, over to the sink, he can reach everything easily.

B Dan pulls a chair over to the sink but reach everything easily.

C Dan pulls a chair over to the sink so that he can reach everything easily.

D Correct as is.

8. Read sentence 5.

Dan likes the lemony smell of the liquid detergent.

What part of speech is the underlined word?

A noun

B pronoun

C verb

D adjective

9. What is the **best** way to combine sentences 6 and 7?

A Squeezing the bottle gently and watching the liquid soap stream into the water.

B He squeezes the bottle gently, watches the liquid soap stream into the water.

C He squeezes the bottle gently and watches the liquid soap stream into the water.

D The liquid soap stream into the water he watches and squeeze the bottle gently.

10. Read sentence 10.

Dan makes <u>Dan's</u> work fun!

What is the correct pronoun to replace the underlined noun?

A his

B him

C he

D hes

Name ______________________________ Date ______________

On your answer sheet, darken the circle for each correct answer.

11. What word completes the sentence?

> I set ______ backpack on his desk.

A Sam's

B Sams'

C Samses

D Sam

12. What word completes the sentence?

> My best friend ______ coming to the beach with me.

A is

B are

C will

D can't

13. What verb correctly completes the sentence?

> Mr. Cho ______ the school band next year.

A will leading

B will lead

C led

D did lead

14. Read these sentences.

> Did you hear that Ryan is moving to Spain? Their last day is Monday.

What word should be used in place of Their?

A Him

B His

C She

D He

15. What word **best** completes this sentence?

> The boy and girl are with ______ parents.

A they're

B them

C there

D their

Name ________________________________ Date ____________________

On your answer sheet, darken the circle for each correct answer.

16. In which sentence is the underlined word or words used correctly?

A We will try to get to school more earlier.

B Ashton has the furtherer to travel.

C Sofia and Erika will have to work harder.

D Mateo was fastest than Geri.

17. Which sentence uses the underlined word or words correctly?

A Terell did worse on the test than Kaitlyn.

B Isabella dances gracefullest than Frieda.

C Caleb came to the party lastest than Joshua.

D Jayden is the most slower runner we know.

18. Which sentence has no error?

A Your not going to eat my apple.

B I could of eaten two more apples!

C I hardly ever eat strawberries.

D I like apples more better then strawberries.

19. In which sentence is the underlined word used correctly?

A The squirrel changed it's mind, turned, and ran back up the tree.

B With its tail wagging, the puppy begged me to take it home.

C Its lots of fun to take pictures of animals in nature.

D Its' been a long summer, so it certainly is nice to have cooler days.

20. Which sentence is written correctly?

A It was time home for the children to go.

B To go home for the children it was time.

C For the children to go home it was time.

D It was time for the children to go home.

Name ______________________________ Date ______________

Read the passage. Then, answer the questions. On your answer sheet, darken the circle for each correct answer.

(1) I got a book of poems from the library. **(2)** The book's title is Poems of the seasons. **(3)** My favorite poem is about summer fall winter and spring. **(4)** Its a poem about how the seasons change. **(5)** The poem is my friend's favorite, too. **(6)** She said, I love that poem!

21. What is the correct way to write sentence 2?

A The book's title is poems of the seasons.

B The book's title is Poems of the Seasons.

C The book's title is Poems Of The Seasons.

D Correct as is.

22. What is the correct way to write sentence 3?

A My favorite poem is about summer, fall, winter, and spring.

B My favorite poem is about summer fall winter, and spring.

C My favorite poem is about, summer, fall winter and spring.

D Correct as is.

23. What is the correct way to write sentence 4?

A Its a poem about how the seasons change?

B Its a poem, about, how the seasons change.

C It's a poem about how the seasons change.

D Correct as is.

24. What is the correct way to write sentence 5?

A The poem is my friends favorite, too.

B The poem is my friends' favorite, too.

C The poem is my friend favorite, too.

D Correct as is.

25. What is the correct way to write sentence 6?

A She said, "I love that poem!"

B She said, I love that poem!

C "She said, I love that poem!"

D Correct as is.

Name ______________________________ Date ______________

Read the passage. Then, answer the questions. On your answer sheet, darken the circle for each correct answer.

(1) We went camping at Mammoth Cave, kentucky. **(2)** We arrived on August 22 2013. **(3)** First, we looked for a place to put our boat on the river. **(4)** Then, we got our fishing poles and our bait. **(5)** "Let's paddle out onto the beautiful blue water, Dad said. **(6)** I caught a bass and a bluegill. **(7)** Later, we dug a pit and started a fire **(8)** We got the fish ready and Dad cooked them for dinner. **(9)** Tomorow, we will take an underground cave tour.

26. What change should be made in sentence 1?

A Capitalize *camping*

B Capitalize *kentucky*

C Lowercase *Mammoth Cave*

D Correct as is.

27. What is the correct way to write sentence 2?

A We arrived on August 22, 2013.

B We arrived on August, 22 2013.

C We arrived on August 22. 2013.

D Correct as is.

28. What is the correct way to punctuate sentence 5?

A Delete the apostrophe in *Let's*

B Add quotation marks after *out*

C Add quotations marks after *water,*

D Correct as is.

29. What is the correct way to punctuate sentence 8?

A Add a comma after *and*

B End with a question mark.

C Add a comma after *them*

D Add a comma after *ready*

30. Read sentence 9.

Tomorow, we will take an underground cave tour.

Which word is misspelled?

A Tomorow

B underground

C cave

D tour

Name ______________________________ Date ______________

On your answer sheet, darken the circle for each correct answer.

31. What is the correct ending punctuation for this sentence?

Have you ever been to Mexico

A .

B ?

C !

D ,

32. Read this sentence.

I like a snack of whole wheet bread and peanut butter.

Which word is misspelled?

A whole

B wheet

C bread

D butter

33. Choose the correctly spelled word to complete the sentence.

Is that ______ new bicycle?

A yore

B you're

C your

D youre

34. Choose the sentence that has correct capitalization.

A We start school in september.

B The american flag was raised on the flagpole.

C Isn't that dr. Jackson?

D I shop at a store called Pottery Palace.

35. What correctly completes the sentence?

Charlotte's Web was written by

A E.B. White.

B e.b. White.

C E.b. White.

D e.b. white.

Name ______________________________ Date ______________

On your answer sheet, darken the circle for each correct answer.

36. Which sentence contains errors?

A Ian said, "Let's play a game of basketball after school."

B I need to return the book Storm Track to the library.

C Did you see the Big Tomatoes growing in Mrs. Garzas garden?

D "This is the funniest book I have ever read," Ava said.

37. Which sentence uses commas correctly?

A We will take tests in reading math, and writing, next week.

B We will take tests in reading, math, and writing next week.

C We will take tests in reading, math, and, writing next week.

D We will take tests in reading math, and writing next week.

38. Which sentence is correct?

A Jacob asked, "Would you like to go skating with me?"

B "Jacob asked, Would you like to go skating with me?"

C "Jacob asked," Would you like to go skating with me?

D "Jacob asked," "Would you like to go skating with me?"

39. Which sentence is correct?

A Dr. Seuss wrote the cat in the hat.

B The olympics were once held in Atlanta Georgia

C My friend lives in Albany, New York.

D Where are you going.

40. Which sentence is correct?

A Can all dogs bark!

B My aunt went to the mall

C My Birthday is in april.

D "Watch out!" yelled Mason.

Name ____________________ Date ____________

Taking Vocabulary Tests

In the Vocabulary Practice section, you will get ready to take vocabulary tests. You will read about how to answer different kinds of questions. Then, you will be asked to read stories and passages and answer questions. You will also be asked to answer stand-alone questions.

Tips for Vocabulary

Using Context Clues

You can use context clues to figure out the meaning of an unknown word. Context clues are words and sentences around the word. Use the following steps to answer questions about context clues:

Step 1: Read the sentence with the unknown word. See if the words before or after it give clues to the word's meaning. Then, read sentences around the word and look for clues.

Step 2: Use the clues to guess the word's meaning.

Step 3: Check your answer by using it in the sentence in place of the unknown word.

Using Word Parts

Many words are made up of more than one word part. A **root word** is a word that does not have any prefixes or suffixes added. For example, the root word of builder is build. A **prefix** is added to the beginning of a word to make a new word. A prefix changes the meaning of the root word. A **suffix** is added to the end of a word to create a new word. A suffix also changes the meaning of the root word.

Prefixes

Prefix	**Meaning**
re-	again
un-	not, the opposite of
dis-	opposite
pre-	before

Prefix		**Root Word**		**New Word**	**Meaning**
re	+	count	=	recount	count again
un	+	certain	=	uncertain	not certain
dis	+	agree	=	disagree	opposite of agree
pre	+	school	=	preschool	before elementary school

Name ______________________ Date ______________

Suffixes

Suffix	Meaning
-less	without
-ful	full of
-y	state or quality of
-ly	in a certain way

Root Word		Suffix		New Word	Meaning
care	+	less	=	careless	without care
color	+	ful	=	colorful	full of color
rock	+	y	=	rocky	the state of having many rocks
bright	+	ly	=	brightly	in a bright way

Identifying Antonyms and Synonyms

Antonyms are words that have opposite meanings.

calm / excited
better / worse

Synonyms are words with the same or nearly the same meaning.

unusual / odd
narrow / tight / thin

Name ______________________________ Date ____________________

Analyzing Multiple-Meaning Words

Some words have more than one meaning. To decide on the correct meaning of a multiple-meaning word, think about whether it is a noun or a verb. Then read the words and sentences around it to look for clues.

The train travels on tracks from Boston to Baltimore.

Train is a noun. Clues are travels and tracks. Train means "a kind of transportation with an engine and cars."

With practice, you can train your dog to follow simple commands.

Train is a verb. Clues are practice and follow commands. Train means "teach or instruct."

Use these steps to choose the correct meaning of a multiple-meaning word:

Step 1: Think about whether the word is a noun or a verb.

Step 2: Read the words and sentences around it to look for clues.

Step 3: Check your definition to see if it makes sense in the sentence.

Name ______________________________ Date ______________

Vocabulary

Read the passage. Then, answer the questions. On your answer sheet, darken the circle for each correct answer.

Just imagine! If big rocks had not been broken into little bits, we would not have any food to eat. That is because all the soil on Earth—the dirt in which we plant flowers and vegetables and grain—is formed largely from rocks. These rocks have been ground by wind, rain, and storms. Of course, many other things are mixed with the crushed rocks to make rich soil. It took hundreds of thousands of years to make our soil.

Some soil is full of pebbles that are larger than grains of sand. This soil is called gravel. Other soil is sandy. Some other soil, called clay, is made up of bits even smaller than sand. These bits are so small that you can hardly see them.

Name ______________________ Date ______________

1. Read this sentence from the passage.

> That is because all the soil on Earth—the dirt in which we plant flowers and vegetables and grain—is formed largely from rocks.

What clue word helps the reader know what soil means?

A dirt

B grain

C wind

D rocks

2. Which definition of ground is used in the sentence below?

> **ground** (ground)
> *noun*
> 1. the solid part of Earth's surface
> *noun*
> 2. the background of a painting
> *verb*
> 3. kept planes from flying
> *verb*
> 4. crushed into tiny parts

> These rocks have been ground by wind, rain, and storms.

A definition 1

B definition 2

C definition 3

D definition 4

3. What two words in the passage have opposite meanings?

A smaller/larger

B rocks/bits

C rain/storms

D pebbles/sand

Name ______________________________ Date ________________

Read the passage. Then, answer the questions. On your answer sheet, darken the circle for each correct answer.

Anita was excited! This was the day she had been waiting for. Anita's Little League coach told her that she was going to be the starting pitcher for the play-off game. Her brothers had been practicing with her and giving her tips on pitching.

Anita was so nervous that she could hardly eat breakfast. "I'm as nervous as a long-tailed cat in a room full of rocking chairs," she thought. Anita decided to talk to the coach before the game.

Anita showed Coach her shaking hands and asked how she could possibly pitch. He reminded her of how well she had done in previous games. He showed her how a deep breath could be calming.

When they got to the baseball park, Coach suggested that Anita look for her dad. She could remember how much he believed in her. She saw her dad looking for a place to watch the game. She called to him. He smiled and waved. Then, she walked to the mound, thought about other games she'd played, took a deep breath, and calmly threw the first ball.

Name ______________________ Date ______________

4. Read the sentence from the passage.

> Anita's Little League coach told her that she was going to be the starting pitcher for the play-off game.

What does pitcher mean?

A the opposite of pitch

B one who pitches

C can be pitched

D related to pitching

5. Read this sentence from the passage.

> "I'm as nervous as a long-tailed cat in a room full of rocking chairs," she thought.

What do the underlined words mean?

A Chairs make Anita nervous.

B Anita is afraid of cats.

C Anita feels very nervous.

D Anita wishes she were a cat.

6. Read this sentence from the passage.

> When they got to the baseball park, Coach suggested that Anita look for her dad.

Which sentence uses park the same way it is used in the passage?

A The batter hit the ball out of the park!

B Park your truck in the driveway.

C We couldn't find anywhere to park downtown.

D He went swimming at the state park.

7. Which definition of watch is used in the sentence below?

> **watch** (woch)
> *verb*
> 1. to view with interest
> *verb*
> 2. to be careful
> *noun*
> 3. a small object that tells time
> *noun*
> 4. a person or group that keeps guard

> She saw her dad looking for a place to watch the game.

A definition 1

B definition 2

C definition 3

D definition 4

Name ______________________ Date ______________

On your answer sheet, darken the circle for each correct answer.

8. Choose the word that **best** completes the sentence.

> He was so thirsty that he ______ the water!

A sipped

B tasted

C gulped

D sampled

9. Which word belongs in this group?

> pond, lake, sea, ______

A ocean

B mountain

C beach

D bathtub

10. Choose the word with a meaning that fits both sentences.

> Doing ______ can help you stay healthy.
> We do math ______ to practice multiplying.

A sit-ups

B exercises

C problems

D hikes

11. Read the sentence.

> I got a reward when I returned the purse I found.

What word means the **same as** reward?

A number

B prize

C trick

D parent

Name ________________________________ Date ________________

On your answer sheet, darken the circle for each correct answer.

12. Read this sentence.

> It is unusual for our teacher to miss school.

What does the word unusual mean?

A not normal

B very normal

C sometimes normal

D always normal

13. Read the sentences.

> What a gloomy day! I can't wait for the heavy clouds to break up.

The underlined word means

A bright.

B cheerful.

C sunny.

D dark.

14. Read this sentence.

> Sophia put the damp clothes on the line to dry.

Which word means about the **same as** damp?

A old

B torn

C wet

D cold

15. Which word **best** completes the sentence?

> I felt _____ so I took a nap.

A awake

B asleep

C tired

D wakeful

Writing
Test Tips and Practice

Name ______________________ Date ______________

Taking Writing Tests

In the Writing Practice section, you will take some practice writing tests. You will read some tips that will help you respond to writing prompts. You will also see graphic organizers you can use to plan your writing. Then, you will practice responding to three writing prompts: opinion, informative, and narrative.

Scoring Writing Prompts

The writing prompts will be scored on a 4-point scale. The writing prompts will be scored for content, organization, and conventions. If a response cannot be read, makes no sense, has too little information to be scored, or is blank, it will not receive any score. Ask your parent or teacher if you need help understanding the 4-point scale.

Scoring on a 4-point Scale

The following explains how your writing will be scored on a 4-point scale.

A ***4-point*** response demonstrates **advanced** success with the writing task. The essay:

- focuses consistently on the topic
- shows effective organization throughout, with smooth transitions
- offers thoughtful ideas
- develops ideas thoroughly, using examples and details
- shows good control of written language

A ***3-point*** response demonstrates **competent** success with the writing task. In general, the essay:

- focuses mostly on the topic
- shows effective organization, with minor lapses
- offers mostly thoughtful ideas
- develops ideas adequately and uses some general and some specific reasons and evidence
- shows general control of written language

Name ______________________________ Date ______________

A ***2-point*** response demonstrates **limited** success with the writing task. In general, the essay:

- includes some ideas that are related to the topic but do not focus consistently on the topic
- shows some organization, with noticeable gaps in the logical flow of ideas
- offers predictable ideas
- develops or supports ideas with little elaboration and reasoning
- shows limited control of written language

A ***1-point*** response demonstrates **emerging** effort with the writing task. In general, the essay:

- shows little awareness of the topic
- lacks organization
- offers confusing ideas
- develops ideas in a minimal way, if at all, or gives only a few reasons
- shows major problems with control of written language

Tips for Responding to a Writing Prompt

- First, **read the prompt carefully**. Be sure that you understand exactly what the prompt is asking.
- **Decide what kind of response you are being asked to write. You should ask yourself, "What is the purpose of this response?"** For example, are you asked to write a story or to explain something? When you understand the type of response you are being asked to write, you will have a sense of the purpose of your response.
- **Decide who your audience is. Ask yourself, "Who is going to read this?"** You might write differently for a friend than you would write for the school principal.
- **Decide on your topic.** Choose only one topic to write about. Make sure your topic is stated as your main idea. Then, make sure all the details and events support that one topic.

Name ______________________________ Date ______________

- Before you begin writing, **plan**. Use a graphic organizer to plan what you want to write. This is the time to think about what you want to say before you begin writing your response.
- Many tests are timed. Before you begin writing, **think about how much time you have**. Usually, allow about one-third of the time to plan your response, about one-third to write a first draft, and about one-third to edit and write a final version. Remember that time spent planning makes the writing part much easier.
- Write in **complete sentences**. Make sure your sentences and paragraphs flow smoothly. Sentences should support the main idea. They should be arranged in an order that makes sense to the reader. Make use of time order words like *first*, *next*, *then*, and *last* if necessary. Write neatly.
- Finally, **proofread your response**. Check for spelling and punctuation errors. Make sure each sentence has a subject and verb. Look over verb tenses to see if you have used them correctly. Make your edits as neat as possible.

These tips can help you do well on the writing section of tests. Remember that practice makes perfect. Read and write as often as possible so your reading and writing get better and better.

Name ______________________________ Date ____________________

Graphic Organizers for Writing

Details Web

A web is helpful when thinking about details. Write your topic in the middle circle. Then write words or phrases that come to mind about the topic in the outer circles.

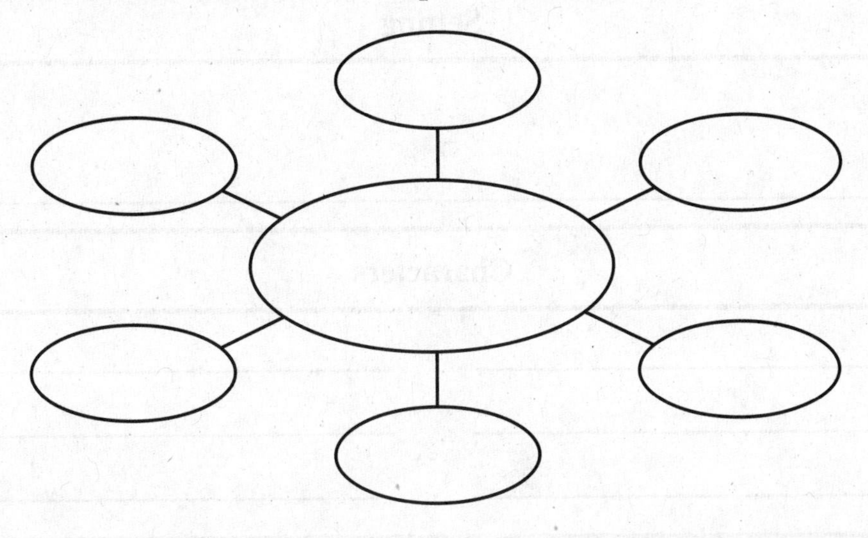

Sequence of Events Chart

A Sequence of Events chart can help you put events or steps in correct order. Use the time order words *first*, *next*, *then*, and *last* in your writing to help the reader understand the order events happen.

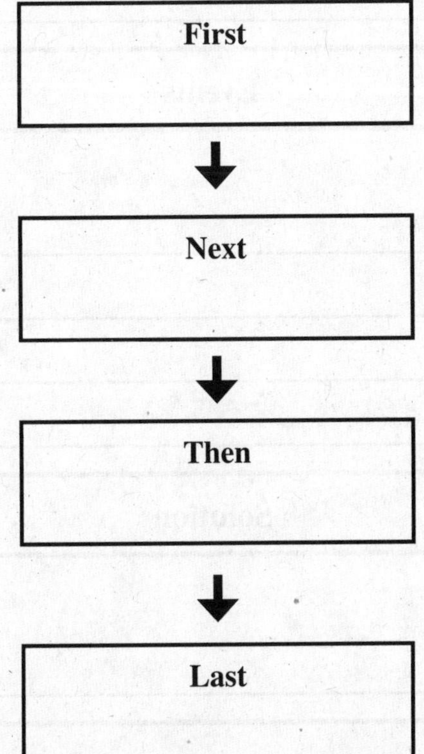

Name ______________________________ Date ______________

Story Map

A Story Map can help you plan the setting, characters, and plot of a story. After you finish the map, use it to make sure your story includes all the story elements.

Setting
____
Characters
______________ ______________ ______________ ______________ ______________ ______________
Problem
____
Events
1. ______________________________ 2. ______________________________ 3. ______________________________ 4. ______________________________
Solution
____

Name ______________________ Date ______________

Main Idea and Details Chart

All of the details in a paragraph need to tell about the main idea or topic of the paragraph. A Main Idea and Details chart can help you keep your topic in mind and make sure all the details you write stick to the topic.

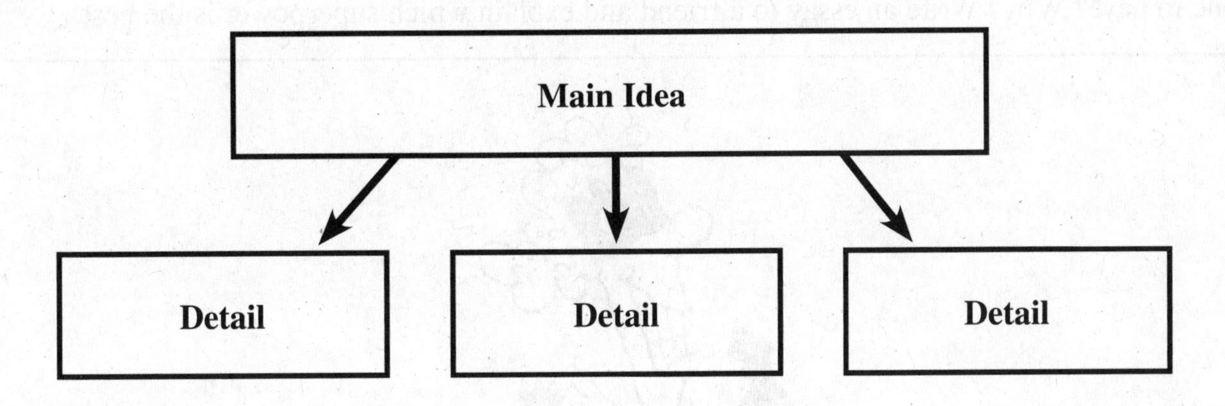

Compare and Contrast Venn Diagram

When you compare and contrast, you tell how things are alike and different. A Venn Diagram like the one below can help you sort how two things are the same and different. Write about one thing in one circle. Write about the other thing in the second circle. Write how they are alike in the middle.

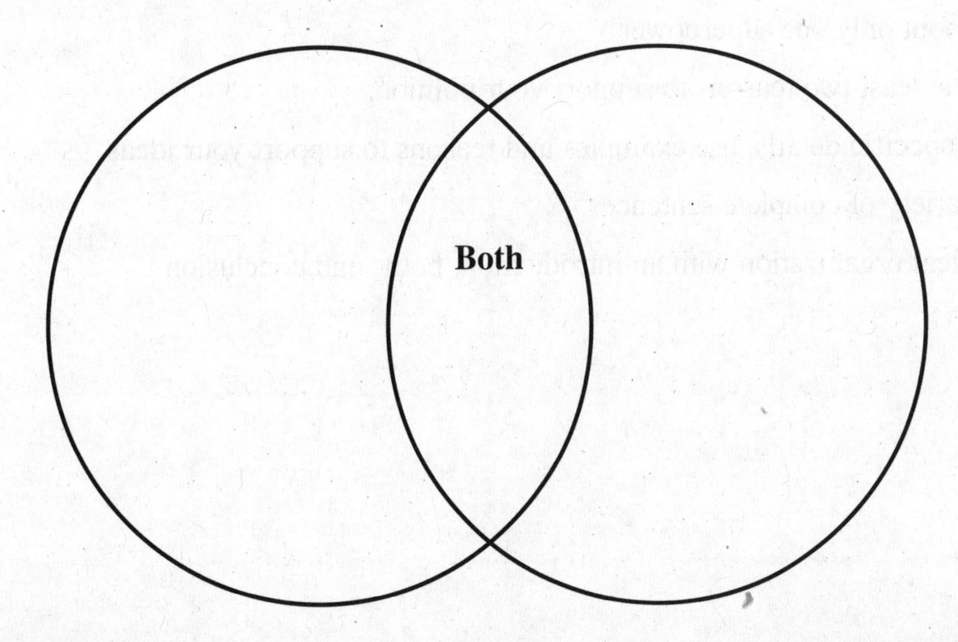

Name ______________________________ Date ______________

Writing Prompt 1: Opinion

Plan your writing and write your response. Then, proofread what you have written.

Think about superheroes and their superpowers. What superpower do you think is the best one to have? Why? Write an essay to a friend and explain which superpower is the best.

As you write your response, be sure to

- Write about only one superpower.
- Include at least two reasons to support your opinion.
- Include specific details; use examples and reasons to support your ideas.
- Use a variety of complete sentences.
- Use logical organization with an introduction, body, and conclusion.

Name ______________________________ Date ______________

Prewriting

1. **Read the Prompt.** Read the prompt carefully. Identify your purpose and your audience.

Purpose and Audience: In the prompt, you are asked to describe to a friend what you think is the best superpower. The prompt tells you your audience. It tells you what you will write about.

Complete the following sentence:

My purpose is to tell ______________________ why I think ______________________ is the best superpower.

Name ______________________________ Date ________________

2. **Provide Details.** As you write, you will describe the best superpower. Use the Writing Details Web below to list details you want to include in your writing.

Write the name of the best superpower in the center circle. Then, write details in the circles around it.

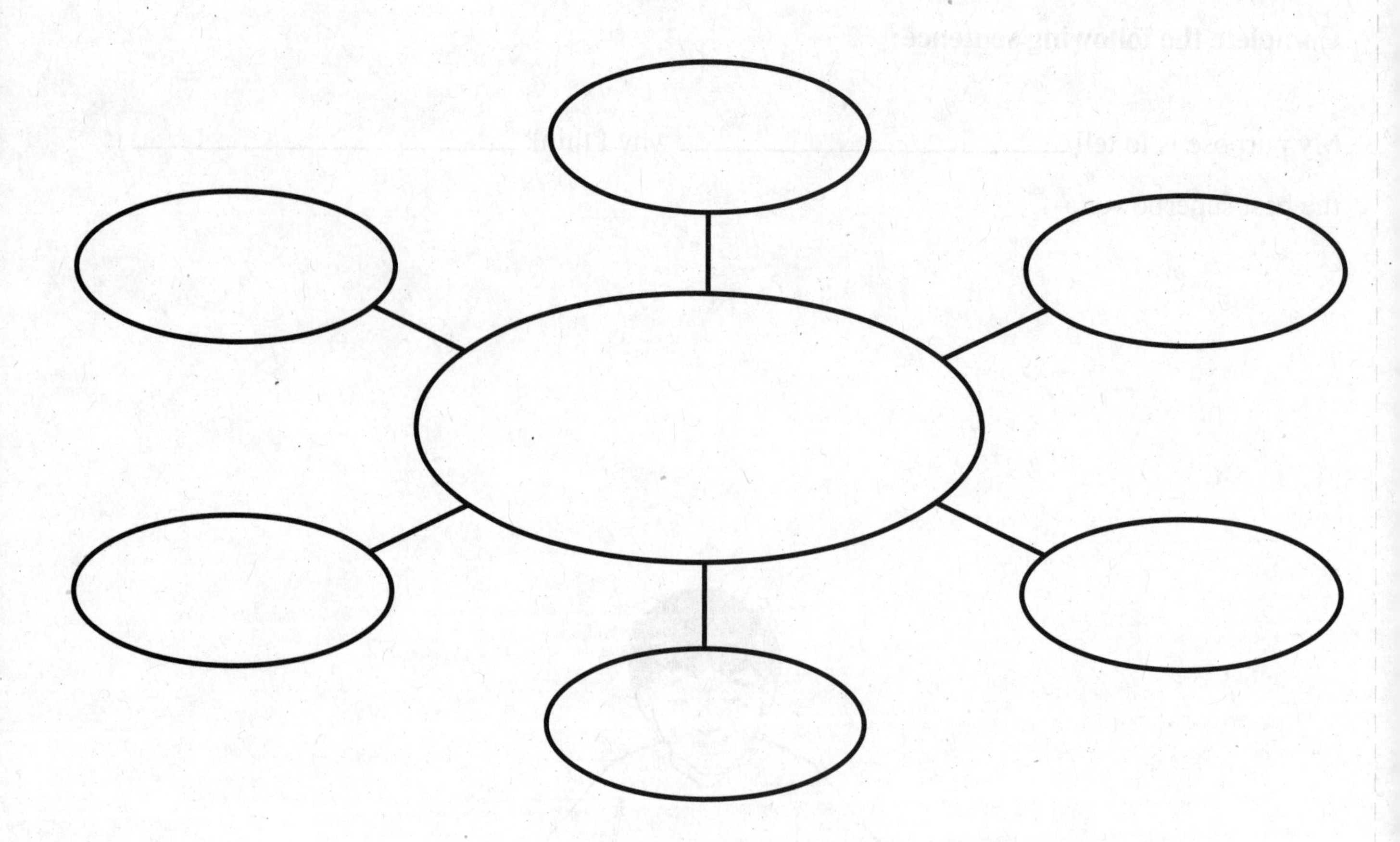

Name ______________________________ Date ______________

3. Organize Your Writing. As you write, you will use the details from the web to describe your topic. You will organize your ideas so that you can present them logically to your audience.

In the organizer below, fill in the superpower you think is the best. Then, add some reasons this superpower is the best one. Use the details that you wrote in the web on page 64 to support each reason. Finally, restate the superpower you think is the best.

My Opinion:

Reason:

____

____

Details to Support My Reason:

____

____

Restate Your Opinion:

Name ______________________ Date ______________

Writing, Editing, and Revising

1. **Draft Your Response.** Use the following chart to help you write a first draft of your essay. Write your draft on your own paper.

Your Essay	Directions and Explanations
	Introduction
• Get your reader's attention right away. • Clearly state your opinion.	**Grab your reader's attention.** Begin with an exciting statement or question that will make your friend want to keep reading. **State your opinion.** Clearly state the topic of your essay in your first paragraph.
	Body
• Give reasons that support your opinion. • Support each reason with clear details.	**Present your ideas.** Write your strongest reason first. Follow it up with two more strong reasons. You may wish to set each reason in its own paragraph. **Support your ideas.** Give details that support each reason. Include examples. Aim to have three reasons in your essay.
	Conclusion
• Remind your reader of your opinion.	**Wrap it up.** Restate your topic, or your main idea. Remind your friend which superpower you think is best.

Name ______________________________ Date ______________

2. **Edit Your Draft.** Now read your response. Answer these questions about your writing. You may make edits on your first draft. You may want to write a second draft on your own paper.

- Does your response state a clear opinion? Does the topic answer the question in the prompt?
- Is your response organized? Does it give reasons why one superpower is your favorite?
- Do you give supporting details for each reason?
- Do the supporting details go with the reason?
- Do you repeat the same words? Can you change any words to clearer, more descriptive words?
- Did you remember your audience? Did you write your response to one friend?

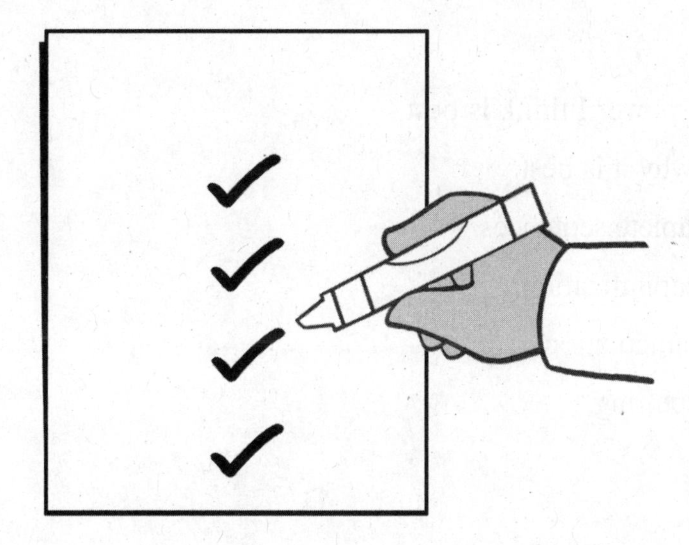

Name ______________________________ Date ________________

3. **Proof Your Draft.** Reread your essay and make sure that it

   - Contains only complete sentences.
   - Has correct subject-verb agreement and uses correct active verbs.
   - Has correct capitalization, punctuation, and spelling.

4. **Write Your Final Response.** On your own paper, write your final response. Use complete sentences.

If you could have any superpower, what would it be? Write an essay in which you describe your superpower. Then, explain to a friend why it is the best superpower to have.

5. **Proofread Your Final Response.** Now, go back to your final response. Use this checklist to check your work one more time.

______ I named a superpower I think is best.

______ I gave reasons why it is best.

______ I used only complete sentences.

______ I used correct capitalization.

______ I used correct punctuation.

______ I used correct spelling.

Name ____________________ Date ____________

Writing Prompt 2: Informative

Plan your writing. Write your response. Then, proofread what you have written.

Think of a time when you had an adventure with a friend. Write an informative essay for a teacher explaining what happened on your adventure.

As you write your response, be sure to

- Write about only one topic.
- Include specific details.
- Use a variety of complete sentences.
- Use a logical organization with an obvious introduction, body, and conclusion.

Name ______________________________ Date ______________

Prewriting

1. **Read the Prompt.** Read the prompt carefully. Identify your purpose and your audience.

Purpose and Audience: In the prompt, you are asked to describe what happened on an adventure you had with a friend. The prompt tells you your audience. It tells you what you will write about.

Complete the following sentence:

My purpose is to tell ______________ what happened when ______________

____

____.

Name ______________________________ Date ______________

2. Plan. As you write, you want to tell exactly what happened on your adventure.

Use the chart below to think about the main details you will use as you write about your adventure. Write an answer to each question on the chart.

What happened?
Who was there?
When did it happen?
Where did it happen?
Why did it happen?

Name ______________________________ Date ______________

3. **Organize Your Writing.** Now that you have thought about some of the details in your adventure, you want to write them in the order they happened.

Use the organizer below to fill in the order of events. Use details from your chart on page 71.

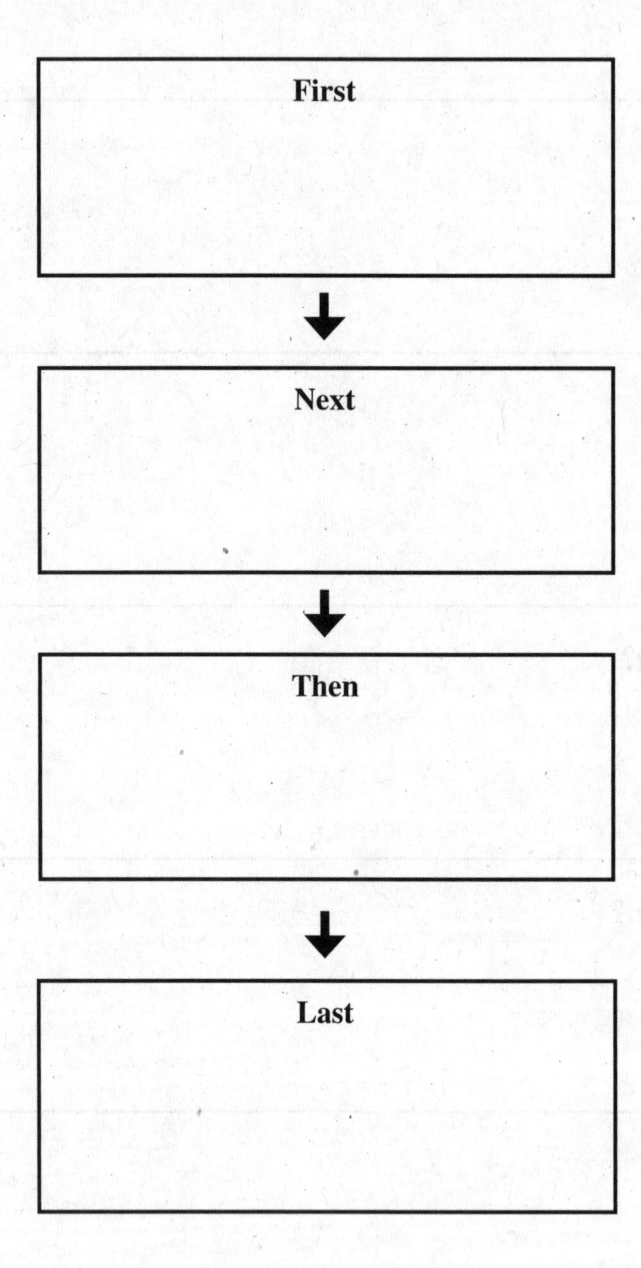

Name ______________________________ Date ______________

Writing, Editing, and Revising

1. **Draft Your Response.** Use the following chart to help you write a first draft of your essay. Write your draft on your own paper.

Your Essay	Directions and Explanations
Introduction	
• Get your reader's attention right away. • Clearly state your main idea.	**Grab your reader's attention.** Begin with an exciting statement or question that will make a teacher want to keep reading. **State your main idea.** Clearly state the topic of your essay in your first paragraph.
Body	
• Explain the main events. • Tell events in order.	**Present your events.** Explain the main events in the body of your essay. **Sequence of events.** Explain what happened by telling events in order. Use order words like *first*, *next*, *then,* and *finally* to make your writing flow and avoid confusing the reader.
Conclusion	
• Remind your reader of your main idea.	**Wrap it up.** Restate your topic, or your main idea. You may wish to conclude your sequence of events at this point.

Name ______________________________ Date ______________

2. **Edit Your Draft.** Now read your response. Ask yourself these questions about your writing. You may make edits on your first draft. You may want to write a second draft on your own paper.

- Does your response state a clear main idea?
- Is your response organized? Does it have a clear sequence of events?
- Do you give supporting details throughout?
- Do you repeat the same words? Can you change any words to clearer, more descriptive words?
- Did you remember your audience? Did you write your response to a teacher?

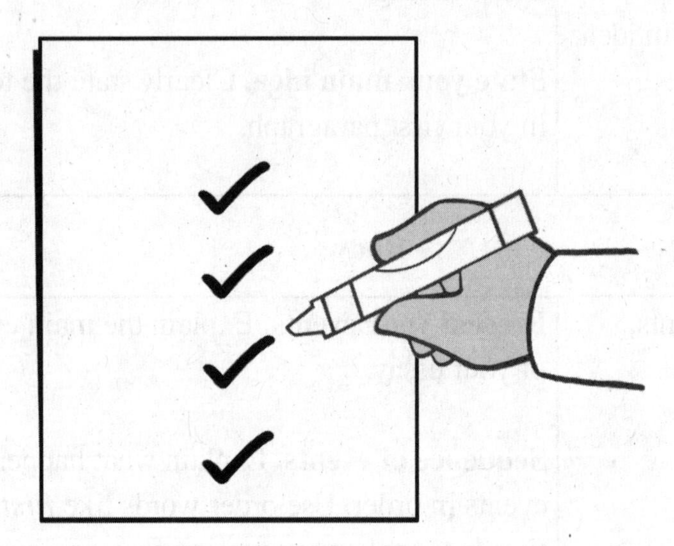

Name ______________________________ Date ______________

3. **Proof Your Draft.** Reread your essay and make sure that it

   - Contains only complete sentences.
   - Has correct subject-verb agreement and uses correct active verbs.
   - Has correct capitalization, punctuation, and spelling.

4. **Write Your Final Response.** On your own paper, write your final response. Use complete sentences.

Think of a time when you had an adventure with a friend. Write an informative essay for a teacher explaining what happened on your adventure.

5. **Proofread Your Final Response.** Now, go back to your final response. Use this checklist to check your work one more time.

______ I clearly stated my main idea.

______ I explained what happened in correct time order.

______ I used only complete sentences.

______ I used correct capitalization.

______ I used correct punctuation.

______ I used correct spelling.

Name ______________________________ Date ______________

Writing Prompt 3: Narrative

Plan your writing. Write your response. Then, proofread what you have written.

If you could be any kind of animal, what animal would you be? Imagine you woke up one morning and you had turned into that animal. Write a story to be read aloud to a first grader about what happened to you that day.

As you write your response, be sure to

- Describe your surroundings and the characters.
- Clearly tell a story that includes descriptive details. Include dialogue, if appropriate.
- Use a variety of complete sentences.
- Use logical organization with an obvious beginning, middle, and end.

Name ______________________________ Date ______________

Prewriting

1. **Read the Prompt.** Read the prompt carefully. Think about your story topic and your audience.

Purpose and Audience: In the prompt, you are asked to tell a story about the day you turned into your favorite animal. The prompt tells you your audience.

Complete the following sentence:

I will write a story for ______________________ about the day I woke up as ______________________.

Name ______________________________ Date ____________________

2. **Plan**. As you write, you want to include details about the setting, the characters, and the plot. Remember, the story plot should include the events, a problem, and a solution to the problem.

Use the Story Map below to organize your story ideas.

Setting
____
Characters
______________ ______________ ______________ ______________ ______________ ______________
Problem
____
Events
1. ______________________________ **2.** ______________________________ **3.** ______________________________ **4.** ______________________________
Solution
____

Name ______________________________ Date ______________

3. **Organize Your Writing.** As you write, you want to tell your story in correct time order.

Use the organizer below to fill in the order of events. Use details from your story map on page 78.

Opening
______________________________ ______________________________
Body (Problem)
1. ______________________________ ______________________________ **2.** ______________________________ ______________________________ **3.** ______________________________ ______________________________ **4.** ______________________________ ______________________________
Ending (solution to problem)
1. ______________________________ **2.** ______________________________

Name ______________________ Date ______________

Writing, Editing, and Revising

1. **Draft Your Response.** Use the following chart to help you write a first draft of your story. Write your draft on your own paper.

Your Story	Directions and Explanations
Introduction	
• Get your reader's attention right away. • Let the audience know what's coming.	**Grab the audience's attention.** Begin with an exciting statement or something that your audience can think about. **Give hints.** Give your audience a hint or two about where the story is going to go.
Body	
• Explain the problem or problems. • Tell events in order.	**Present the problem.** Set up the story problem or problems. Include details to keep the reader interested. **Order of events.** Explain what happened by telling events in correct time order. Use sequence words like *first*, *next*, *then*, and *finally*.
Conclusion	
• End with a solution to the problem.	**Wrap it up.** Make sure the ending leaves the reader with a feeling that the story has ended. Find solutions to all story problems.

Name ______________________________ Date ______________

2. **Edit Your Draft.** Now read your response. Answer these questions about your writing. You may make edits on your first draft. You may want to write a second draft on your own paper.

- Does your story have a clear beginning, middle, and ending?
- Is there a clear sequence of events? Will the reader be able to follow the plot?
- Do you give supporting details throughout?
- Have you wrapped up the story so the problem is solved?
- Do you repeat the same words? Can you change any words to clearer, more descriptive words?
- Did you remember your audience? Did you write your response for a first grader?

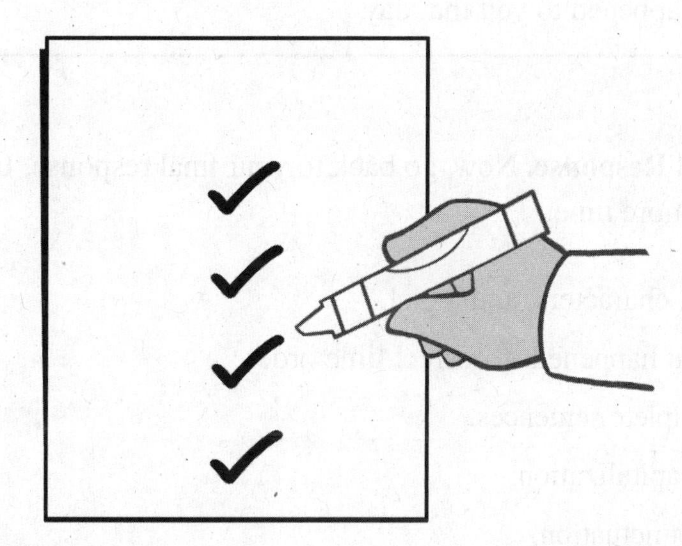

Name ______________________________ Date ____________

3. **Proof Your Draft.** Reread your story and make sure that it

- Contains only complete sentences.
- Has correct subject-verb agreement and uses correct active verbs.
- Has correct capitalization, punctuation, and spelling.

4. **Write Your Final Response.** On your own paper, write your final response. Use complete sentences.

If you could be any kind of animal, what animal would you be? Imagine you woke up one morning and you had turned into that animal. Write a story to be read aloud to a first grader about what happened to you that day.

5. **Proofread Your Final Response.** Now, go back to your final response. Use this checklist to check your work one more time.

______ I have a setting, characters, and a plot.

______ I explained what happened in correct time order.

______ I used only complete sentences.

______ I used correct capitalization.

______ I used correct punctuation.

______ I used correct spelling.

Reading Practice Test

Name ______________________________ Date ______________

Read the story. Then, answer the questions. On your answer sheet, darken the circle for each correct answer for multiple-choice items. For the short-answer item, write your answer on a separate sheet of paper.

A Dance to Remember

Tonight was the opening night of our school's dance performance. Thirty students were in the show. We had practiced for two months to get ready. We wanted the show to be perfect. Everything went well until it was time for the final dance. We heard the music start to play. Maria was supposed to go onstage to dance, but she didn't. We looked everywhere for her, but we couldn't find her. All of the dancers were worried. Where was Maria? We didn't know what to do.

Then the director whispered, "Marcus, you go on!"

"I don't know what to do," I whispered back.

"You're one of the best dancers," she said. "Just pretend you know the dance."

I was very nervous. She wanted me to go onstage and make up a dance. I had never done that before, but I decided to be brave and dance. I walked onstage and saw the audience staring at me. I started dancing. I danced to the beat of the music. I did some dance steps that I had learned in class. I even made up some new movements. I leaned and turned and twisted and skipped. I almost fell down several times. I kept thinking that my dance must have looked ridiculous to the audience.

After a few minutes, I saw Maria dance out onto the stage. That's when I quickly danced off. When I got behind the stage, I felt very relieved.

When the show was over, everyone wanted to know what had happened to Maria. Maria told us that she had gotten locked out of the theater. She had banged on the door, but no one heard her because the music was playing. Then, she found a side door in the courtyard that was open. She had made it onto the stage a few minutes later.

Everyone congratulated me for having the courage to make up a dance on the stage. I'm proud that I was able to help out, but I hope that I never have to do that again!

Name ______________________ Date ______________

1. What would be another good title for this story?

   A Opening Night

   B My Favorite Sport

   C Maria's Vacation

   D Dance Lessons

2. According to the story, why did no one open the door for Maria?

   A All the students were onstage.

   B She was in the girls' room.

   C The audience liked Marcus's dance better.

   D No one could hear her banging on the door.

3. The story is told from the point of view of

   A the director.

   B Maria.

   C Marcus.

   D the narrator.

4. What word **best** describes Marcus?

   A loud

   B timid

   C brave

   D clumsy

5. What will Maria **most likely** do the next time she is in a dance performance?

   A She will wait outside until it is her turn.

   B She will dance all her dances with Marcus.

   C She will play her music very softly.

   D She will stay inside the building near the stage.

6. In your own words, describe what happens to Maria in this story.

Name ____ Date ____________________

Read the story. Then, answer the questions. On your answer sheet, darken the circle for each correct answer for multiple-choice items. For the short-answer item, write your answer on a separate sheet of paper.

What Happened at the Zoo?

Hannah used to live in a large city where she had many friends. When her mother had gotten a job in a small town, Hannah had been upset. She hadn't wanted to move. She hadn't wanted to leave her friends, especially her best friend Sylvia. Hannah's mother had promised that they would arrange a visit with Sylvia soon.

Two months after they moved, Hannah's mother asked her a question. "How would you like to go to the zoo on Saturday?" she said. "I just talked to Mrs. Reyna on the phone. She and Sylvia can meet us there." Hannah was excited. She couldn't think of anything she'd rather do.

The next Saturday was cold and clear. Hannah put on many layers of warm clothing. She grabbed the book she had made for Sylvia. It told about all the fun things they had done when they lived next door to each other.

When Hannah and her mother drove up to the zoo, they saw Sylvia and her mother waiting at the entrance. Hannah ran up and hugged Sylvia and said, "I'm as happy as a mouse in a cheese factory!" Sylvia laughed and then the girls skipped down the path to the monkey house.

"Wait for us at the entrance to the monkey house," Mrs. Reyna said. But the girls were so busy talking that they didn't hear her.

Hannah and Sylvia watched the gorillas for a while. They had never seen such large apes. Then they ran to the area with lions and tigers.

They bought some food for the elephants and fed them. They spent a long time watching a giraffe and its baby.

When they started getting hungry, they turned around to look for their mothers but couldn't find them anywhere. "Uh oh! I think we might be in trouble," Hannah said. Sylvia was worried, too. The girls sat down and tried to think of what to do.

They decided to follow the signs back to the entrance.

Name ______________________________ Date ________________

They walked for a long time. They went past the African animal section, the large cats, and the monkey house before they saw their mothers. "Where have you been? We've been looking everywhere for you!" Hannah's mother said. The girls didn't know what to say.

Later Sylvia whispered to Hannah, "Well, I guess we can add another chapter to the book you wrote. We can write about the time we got lost at the zoo."

7. What is this story **mainly** about?

A Hannah's move to a small town

B Hannah's mother's new job

C a monkey house at a zoo

D two girls' day at a zoo

8. Why were the mothers upset?

A They were tired.

B They were worried.

C They were lost.

D They were hungry.

Name ______________________________ Date ________________

9. In what season does this story **most likely** take place?

A winter

B spring

C summer

D fall

10. Read the following sentence from the story.

> Hannah ran up and hugged Sylvia and said, "I'm as happy as a mouse in a cheese factory!"

How does "happy as a mouse in a cheese factory" tell you that Hanna felt very happy?

A Mice get easily lost, so a mouse could get lost in a large building.

B Mice love to eat cheese, so a mouse would be happy to be in a factory filled with cheese.

C Mice often live in factories, so a mouse would be happy to be inside any kind of factory.

D Cheese can be put in mousetraps, and a cheese factory has lots of cheese for many mousetraps.

11. Which words from the story **best** show that Hannah and Sylvia had gotten far away from their mothers?

A the girls skipped down the path

B Then they ran to the area

C The girls sat down

D They walked for a long time

12. Look at the picture on page 88. What does the picture tell you about the setting?

A The zoo has a snack bar.

B The zoo has tour guides.

C The zoo has a petting zoo.

D All animals in the zoo are in cages.

13. What does the picture on page 88 show about the girls' day?

A The girls had an argument.

B The girls were gone for a long time.

C The girls also fed a goat.

D The girls also had a carrot snack.

14. Why is the book Hannah made important to her and Sylvia?

Name ______________________________ Date ______________

Read the play. Then, answer the questions. On your answer sheet, darken the circle for each correct answer for multiple-choice items. For the short-answer item, write your answer on a separate sheet of paper.

The Last Day of School

Cast

Cathy, Mia, Anna (third-grade girls)

Max, Jerome, José (third-grade boys)

Mrs. Lee (their teacher)

Scene 1

(The girls enter stage right. It is recess. They are going to jump rope.)

Cathy: *(clapping her hands)* I can't wait until summer. Only one more week of school, but it feels like forever!

Mia: I'm so excited! We should celebrate in some way.

Anna: I know! I'll ask my parents if the class can come to my house on the last day of school. We can blow up a million balloons and play games.

Cathy: Cool! We'll help you plan everything.

(The girls are in a group, talking quietly. The boys enter stage left and play ball.)

Max: *(thoughtfully)* I can't believe third grade is almost over.

Jerome: Let's plan a picnic for the last day of school! The class can meet at the park.

José: Yeah! We can bring snacks and play basketball. It will be the best picnic ever!

Name ______________________ Date ______________

Scene 2

(The bell rings. Students return to class and gather around their teacher's desk.)

Anna: Guess what, Mrs. Lee? We're having an end-of-the-year party.

Mrs. Lee: Doesn't that sound wonderful!

Jerome: Anna, how did you know about our plans?

Anna: *Your* plans? We just made plans to have everyone come over to my house.

Jerome: No, everyone is going to go to the park.

Mrs. Lee: Okay. Let's get back to work.

(All students take their seats.)

Scene 3

(After school that same day. All the kids except Anna are walking home.)

Cathy: *(frowning)* How are we going to pick which party to go to?

Max: Yeah, going to Anna's house sounds fun, but so does a picnic.

José: I guess we just have to choose.

Mia: Don't choose yet, José. I might have a way to work it out.

Jerome: Count us in.

Name ______________________________ Date ______________

Scene 4

(Last day of school. The bell has just rung, and Anna and Mia start to walk home.)

Anna: All right, let's run to my house! The others will meet us there.

Mia: The park is right here. Let's just stop for a second.

Anna: Well, okay.

(The rest of the children run on stage.)

Group: Surprise!

Anna: *(looking puzzled)* What's going on?

Mia: We talked to your parents and the boys. They helped us bring all the balloons and games to the park. Are you upset?

Anna: No way! This is great! There's only one problem. *(frowning, placing hands on hips)*

Max: What's that?

Anna: I'm so hungry I could eat a horse! Where are the snacks?

15. Read this sentence from the play.

> We can blow up a million balloons and play games.

What does Anna mean by a million balloons?

A expensive balloons

B 1,000,000 balloons

C a lot of balloons

D really large balloons

16. Read the sentences from the play.

> *(The girls enter stage right. It is recess. They are going to jump rope.)*

The sentences tell the reader

A the setting and how the actors should move.

B what words Mrs. Lee should say.

C where the actors should perform the show.

D what kind of costumes the actors should wear.

Name ______________________ Date ____________

17. How can you tell this passage is a play?

A It has a beginning, middle, and ending.

B It has speeches for characters to say.

C It has rhythm and rhyme.

D It includes characters' feelings.

18. Why do the children want to have a party?

A to mark the end of summer

B to honor their teacher

C to see Anna's new house

D to celebrate the end of school

19. What does the author **mainly** use to tell what happens in the play?

A a narrator

B illustrations

C characters' speech

D breaking into scenes

20. In Scene 4, why did Anna look puzzled and ask what was going on?

A Anna didn't want to stop at the park.

B Anna didn't think the plan looked like her plan.

C The children shouting "Surprise!" upset Anna.

D Anna wanted to know where the food was.

21. List two differences between the girls' plan and the boys' plan.

Name ______________________________ Date ________________

Read the poem. Then, answer the questions. On your answer sheet, darken the circle for each correct answer for multiple-choice items. For the short-answer item, write your answer on a separate sheet of paper.

Wish

Saturday I flew my kite
on a hilltop high.
I wish I could soar like that
up in the clear blue sky.
I wish I was a darting bird
and could come and go at will.

Sail anywhere I want
over my town, the river, and hill.
I wish to be a cloud
that drifts without a care.
Beyond trouble's reach,
you could find me happy there.

Name ______________________________ Date ______________

22. How does the idea of flying make the speaker feel?

A smart

B sad

C free

D bored

23. Where does this poem **most likely** take place?

A near a small town

B inside a big city

C deep in a forest

D on the ocean

24. What is the theme of this poem?

A Kite flying is safe when free of power lines.

B Being free of all troubles and cares brings happiness.

C Darting birds can fly as high as kites and clouds.

D Kites can teach people about how flight takes place.

25. Read the lines from the poem.

> Saturday I flew my kite
> on a hilltop high.
> I wish I could soar like that
> up in the clear blue sky.

These lines are an example of

A a character.

B theme.

C rhyme.

D a sentence fragment.

26. Which line **best** supports the poem's lesson?

A Saturday I flew my kite

B up in the clear blue sky

C over my town, the river, and hill

D Beyond trouble's reach

27. What things in nature did the speaker use to explain his or her wish?

Name ______________________________ Date ______________

Read the poem. Then, answer the questions. On your answer sheet, darken the circle for each correct answer for multiple-choice items. For the short-answer item, write your answer on a separate sheet of paper.

If I Were Older

If I were older,
I'd climb up that tree
And sit way up on top.
Then I'd look down and see
The world all around
Buildings and tiny houses
So close to the ground.
I'd see cars and trucks go whizzing by
Some go so fast, they almost fly.
And I would smile
As I sat up so high.
And in a little while
I'd touch the sky.

Name ______________________________ Date ______________

28. The speaker in this poem is **most likely**

A a man.

B a woman.

C a child.

D a pet.

29. Why would the buildings and houses look tiny?

A The speaker is up high.

B They are close to the ground.

C They are near the tree.

D The speaker is older.

30. Which could be another title for this poem?

A Climbing Rocks

B View from a Treetop

C Cars Whiz By

D Building Tree Houses

31. Read this line from the poem.

> I'd see cars and trucks
> go <u>whizzing by</u>

What do the underlined words mean?

A parking near each other

B in a traffic jam

C stopping and starting

D going so fast they make a *whiz* sound

32. Which of the following lines from the poem rhyme?

1	Then I'd look down and see
2	The world all around
3	Buildings and tiny houses
4	So close to the ground.

A lines 2 and 4

B lines 1 and 2

C lines 2 and 3

D lines 1 and 4

33. How does the speaker of the poem feel about growing up?

Name ______________________________ Date ______________

Read the passage. Then, answer the questions. On your answer sheet, darken the circle for each correct answer for multiple-choice items. For the short-answer item, write your answer on a separate sheet of paper.

Climbing Everest

By Micheala Ruben

Mount Everest is the world's highest mountain. It is part of the Himalayan Mountains of South Asia. It is over 29,000 feet tall. That is nearly 5-1/2 miles!

Everest is more than just tall. It is also very, very cold. Much of it is covered with snow and ice. Storms and blizzards often strike. Fierce winds blow. There are avalanches, too.

Many people think that it is the hardest mountain in the world to climb. For centuries, no one even tried. Long ago, the people who lived near Everest believed that the mountains were sacred. They thought that their gods lived in the mountains. Therefore, they did not want to climb them. Then in the 1900s, people started coming from around the world. They came to explore the Himalayas. The local people helped them. Together, they began climbing.

In 1921, a British explorer tried to climb Everest. His name was George Mallory. He did not succeed. He tried again in 1922 and 1924. On his last trip, he almost made it to the top. He slipped and fell, though. No one ever saw him alive again.

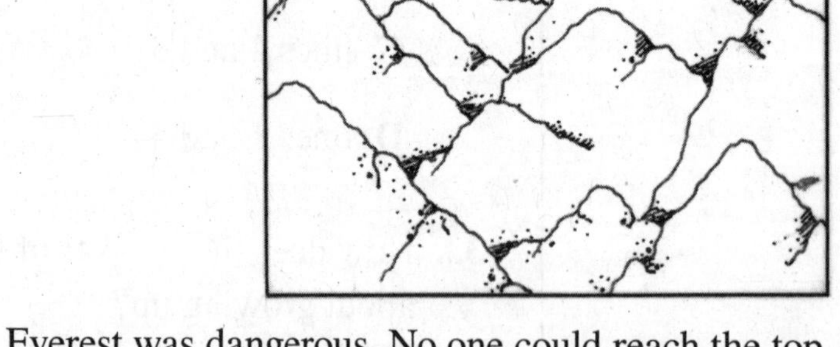

Everest was dangerous. No one could reach the top. Even so, people kept trying. One person who wanted to try was John Hunt. Hunt put together a team. Edmund Hillary was one of his climbers. Hillary grew up in New Zealand. He learned to climb there.

Hunt's team also included Tenzing Norgay. He was from the country of Nepal, near Everest. He joined the British climbing teams to Everest in the 1930s. By 1952, he had climbed more of Everest than anyone else. Together, Hillary and Norgay would make history.

Name ______________________________ Date ______________

The Hunt team climbed Everest in 1953. The mountain was too much of a challenge for most of them. All but two turned back. Hillary and Norgay kept going. On May 29, they reached the top.

When Hillary and Norgay came down, they were famous. They had climbed Everest! Hillary went on to explore in Antarctica. Norgay helped direct a school for mountain climbing. Both men wrote books about their adventures.

Today, people know that Mount Everest can be climbed. Thousands have tried, and hundreds have made it to the top. Yet people will always remember Hillary and Norgay. They were the first to reach Everest's peak.

34. Which sentence **best** tells what the passage is about?

A Mount Everest is a tall and dangerous mountain that often gets strong blizzards and avalanches.

B Hillary and Norgay taught people how to climb mountains, including Mount Everest.

C Hillary and Norgay reached the top of Mount Everest in 1953, and other people have tried before and since.

D Hillary and Norgay both wrote books about their adventures.

35. Why did the people who lived near Everest start climbing in the Himalayas?

A to help climbers from around the world

B to find George Mallory

C to see the top of a sacred mountain

D to become famous

36. Why did the author write "Climbing Everest"?

A to teach readers how to climb tall mountains like Everest

B to warn readers about the dangers of climbing Everest

C to tell readers about Everest and the people who climbed it

D to tell readers about the people who live around Everest

37. The author would **most likely** agree that

A climbing Everest is foolish and dangerous.

B climbing Everest is an amazing adventure.

C climbing Everest has lost its excitement since 1953.

D no one has successfully climbed Everest since 1953.

Name ______________________________ Date ______________

38. Read this sentence from the passage.

> In 1921, a British explorer tried to climb Everest.

The word explorer means a

A person who likes cold weather.

B person who likes to spend time outside.

C person who studies science to learn new things.

D person who travels to new places to learn about them.

39. How is most of the information in this passage organized?

A what happened and why it happened

B time order

C compare and contrast

D problem and solution

40. Name three people who have tried to climb Mount Everest and describe what happened to each.

Name ________________________________ Date ________________

Read the passage. Then, answer the questions. On your answer sheet, darken the circle for each correct answer for multiple-choice items. For the short-answer item, write your answer on a separate sheet of paper.

Bird Migration

In the winter, most birds fly south so they can live in warmer climates. Birds have been known to fly nonstop across oceans and seas. These flights may not be reported in the news, but they are quite amazing. Just think about how tiny some of these birds are!

One bird called the Arctic tern gives birth to its young near the North Pole. When their fledglings are old enough, the Arctic terns fly to islands near the South Pole. They cross many oceans and many lands. In fact, they spend about half their lives flying.

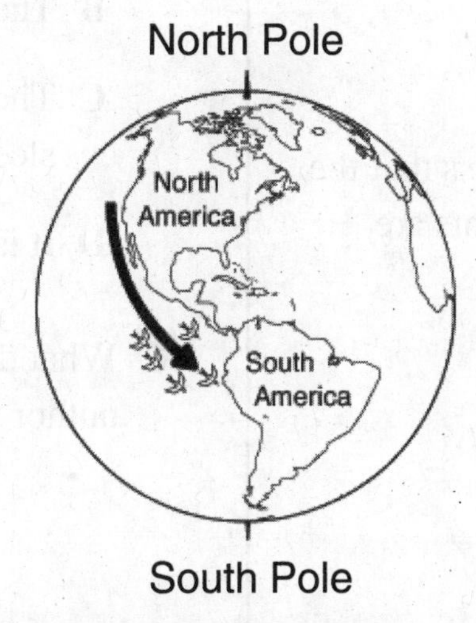

Arctic terns fly over both North America and South America on the way to their winter home near the South Pole.

Robins and bluebirds don't fly so far. They spend their winters in the middle states. Orioles and tiny hummingbirds fly down to Mexico and Central America.

Name ________________________________ Date ______________

41. Read this sentence from the passage.

> One bird called the Arctic tern gives birth to its young near the North Pole. When their fledglings are old enough, the Arctic terns fly to islands near the South Pole.

Another word for fledglings is

A babies.

B mothers.

C fathers.

D parents.

42. From this passage, you can guess that the birds that make the longest flights are

A robins.

B Arctic terns.

C bluebirds.

D hummingbirds.

43. What is another good title for this passage?

A Birds That Make Nonstop Ocean Flights

B How Birds Fly

C Where Some Birds Spend the Winter

D The Arctic Tern

44. How can you tell what continents the Arctic tern fly over?

A read the first paragraph

B read the second paragraph

C use the map and caption

D use an encyclopedia

45. Why do most birds fly south in the winter?

A They need warm weather.

B They follow the way the wind blows.

C They need to spend the winter sleeping.

D It is a mystery.

46. What does the passage say that shows the author thinks birds' flights are great?

Name ______________________________ Date ______________

Read the passage. Then, answer the questions. On your answer sheet, darken the circle for each correct answer for multiple-choice items. For the short-answer item, write your answer on a separate sheet of paper.

Talking on a String

At the Save Our Planet Club, we are always looking for new ways to reuse and recycle everyday materials. Here's a fun way you can reuse cans to make a telephone.

Materials:

- 2 cans, about the same size, clean and empty; each can has one lid removed
- hammer and nail
- pencil

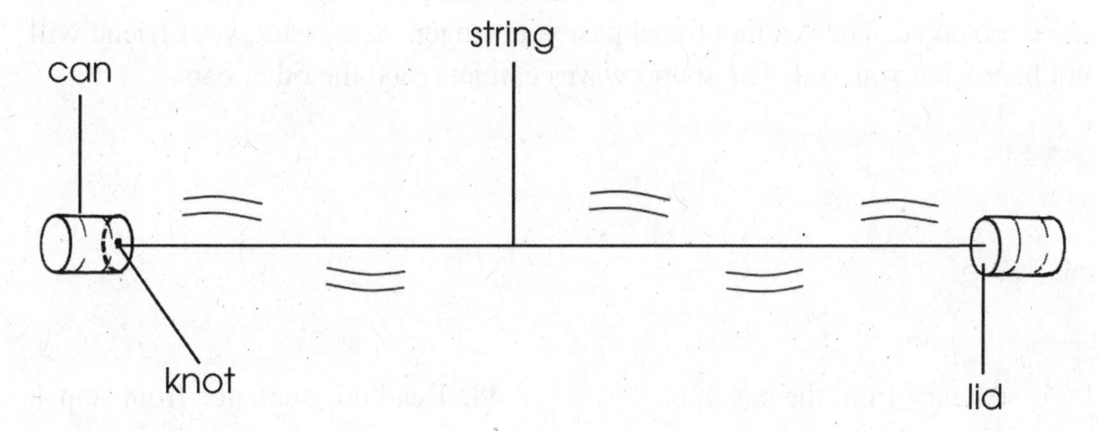

What to Do

1. Find an adult to help you.
2. Gather all your materials.
3. Place your cans on the ground with the open ends facing down. Mark a spot in the center of each lid. Then, ask the adult to help you punch a hole through the marked spot with a hammer and a nail in the lid of each can.
4. Push one end of the string through the hole in one of the cans. Use a pencil to push the string through. *Be safe: do not use your finger!* Then, knot the string firmly inside the can.
5. Push the other end of the same string through the hole in the top of the second can and knot it also. You now have a can telephone!

Name ______________________________ Date ______________

How to Use Your Can Telephone

To enjoy your telephone, find a friend. Each of you should hold one can. Pull the string tightly between you, and make sure it does not touch anything. Speak into your can while your friend holds the other can to his or her ear. Then switch roles. Teach others how to make can telephones, and show them that recycling can be fun!

How a Can Telephone Works

Like a real telephone, a can telephone lets sound waves travel back and forth. Sound travels well through a solid, like a piece of string. When one person speaks into the can, the sound makes the string vibrate. The sound waves travel along the string to the other can. When they reach your friend's ear, he or she can hear what you said.

What happens if you pinch the string with your finger? The sound waves are interrupted. They cannot travel past your finger. As a result, your friend will not hear what you said. The sound waves cannot reach the other can.

47. Read this sentence from the passage.

> When one person speaks into the can, the sound makes the string vibrate.

What does vibrate mean in the sentence?

A loose

B carry

C bend

D shake

48. Read this sentence from step 4.

> *Be safe: do not use your finger!*

This sentence is **most likely** in italic print to

A make sure you use your thumb instead of your finger.

B explain that a pencil is the only object that will work with the string.

C stress that it is dangerous to poke your finger through cut metal.

D let you know that the sound waves will not move through your finger.

49. In which section of the passage would you add the step "Wash out the cans before you begin"?

A Materials

B What to Do

C How to Use Your Can Telephone

D How a Can Telephone Works

50. What is the best summary of the "How a Can Telephone Works" section?

A Because sound waves travel through solids, sound travels along the string from one can to another.

B A can telephone has a piece of string that goes back and forth, just like a telephone.

C When you use a telephone, sound waves move back and forth between the people who are talking.

D The string in a can telephone vibrates, but you can't see that when you are using it.

51. How is the information in the "What to Do" section mainly organized?

A Reasons for recycling are given.

B Can telephones are compared to other phones.

C Steps on how to make a phone are given in order.

D Problems with can phones are presented with solutions.

52. Which statement supports the idea that recycling can be fun?

A Gather all your materials.

B Find an adult to help you.

C To enjoy your telephone, find a friend.

D Sound travels well through a solid, like your piece of string.

53. Use information from the passage to complete parts A and B of the web below.

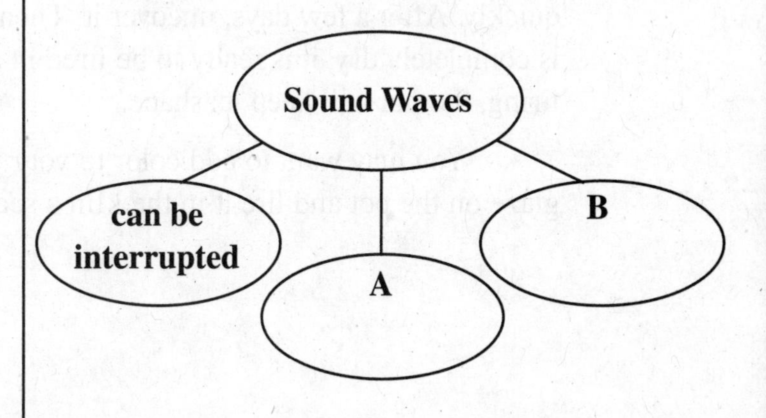

Name ______________________________ Date ________________

Read the passage. Then, answer the questions. On your answer sheet, darken the circle for each correct answer for multiple-choice items. For the short-answer item, write your answer on a separate sheet of paper.

How to Make a Clay Pot

With practice, anyone can make a simple pot from clay. Take a piece of clay the size of an apple and put it on a flat surface. Press and squeeze it until there are no lumps or air bubbles. Then, using both hands, shape the clay into a smooth, round ball.

Now you are ready to begin. Keep the ball in your left hand. With the thumb of your right hand, make an opening in the clay. Press down toward your palm, leaving a half inch of clay at the bottom. This will be the base of your pot. Now keep your thumb inside the pot. Press the clay gently between your thumb and fingers. Turn the pot after each squeeze. This will make the pot thin out evenly. Continue squeezing and turning until the pot is as thin as you want it.

Now the pot must dry. Cover it with plastic so that it won't dry too quickly. After a few days, uncover it. Then, wait a few more days. When the pot is completely dry, it is ready to be fired in a special oven called a kiln. After the firing, the pot will keep its shape.

You may want to add color to your pot. In this case, you would put a glaze on the pot and fire it in the kiln a second time.

Name ______________________________ Date ______________

54. The first thing you should do when making a pot is to

A squeeze out the air bubbles from the clay.

B cover the clay with plastic wrap.

C shape the clay into a ball.

D make the base of the pot.

55. Why should you turn the pot after each squeeze?

A to remove your thumb

B so the pot will have a base

C so the pot will keep its shape

D so the pot won't be thick in some spots

56. Why can't you make a clay pot in one day?

A Clay must rest after each step in making a pot.

B Making a clay pot is too complicated to do quickly.

C It must dry for days and then be fired in a kiln.

D It takes two days just to press out lumps and make a ball.

57. Read this sentence from the passage.

> When the pot is completely dry, it is ready to be fired in a special oven called a kiln.

What is the meaning of the word fired in this sentence?

A shot

B baked

C had to leave a job

D made someone excited

58. Which of these statements should you include in a good summary of "How to Make a Clay Pot"?

A Anyone can make a clay pot.

B Use your right hand.

C Now you are ready to begin making the pot.

D Squeeze and turn the clay until you form a pot.

59. When would a pot be fired twice?

A when it is glazed

B when it is not dry

C when it has a thick base

D when it has an air bubble

60. Which step of making a clay pot should an adult do? Why?

Language Arts and Vocabulary Practice Test

Name ______________________ Date ______________

Language Arts

Read the passage. Then, answer the questions. On your answer sheet, darken the circle for each correct answer.

(1) The California poppy is sometimes called the golden poppy. **(2)** It is a bright yellow color, turning to gold at its center. **(3)** The flower is two or three inch across. **(4)** The plant grows to be two feet tall. **(5)** In the spring, countless numbers of these plants cover California's mountainsides ______ gold. **(6)** In fact, the California poppy ______ the official state flower of California. **(7)** The California Poppy Festival is held every spring. **(8)** It is held in Lancaster, California.

1. Read sentence 1.

The California poppy is sometimes called the golden poppy.

What part of speech is the underlined word?

A verb

B adjective

C pronoun

D noun

2. Read sentence 3.

The flower is two or three inch across.

What is the correct way to write the plural of the underlined word?

A inch's

B inchs

C inches

D Correct as is.

3. Which word goes in the blank in sentence 5?

A for

B under

C during

D with

Name ______________________________ Date ______________

4. Read sentence 6.

In fact, the California poppy _______ the official state flower of California.

What verb **best** completes this sentence?

A is

B are

C be

D were

5. What is the **best** way to combine sentences 7 and 8?

A The California Poppy Festival is held every spring, it is held in Lancaster, California.

B The California Poppy Festival is held every spring in Lancaster, California.

C The California Poppy Festival held every spring and it will be held in Lancaster, California.

D It is held in Lancaster, California and is every spring.

Name ______________________________ Date ______________

Read the passage. Then, answer the questions. On your answer sheet, darken the circle for each correct answer.

(1) Levi is running late for school. **(2)** He forgetted to set his alarm. **(3)** He may not be able to ride the bus _______ school with the other children. **(4)** He gets ready quickly. **(5)** He eat breakfast in a flash! **(6)** Will _______ make it to the bus on time? **(7)** Levi ran full speed the to blocks to the bus stop and boarded the bus!

6. Read sentence 2.

> He forgetted to set his alarm.

What word should replace forgetted?

A forgot

B forgotted

C forgetting

D forget

7. Read sentence 3.

> He may not be able to ride the bus _______ school with the other children.

What word **best** completes the sentence?

A to

B at

C over

D about

Name ______________________________ Date ______________

8. Which word is used incorrectly?

A running in sentence 1

B set in sentence 2

C eat in sentence 5

D time in sentence 6

9. Read sentence 6.

Will _______ make it to the bus on time?

What pronoun **best** completes the sentence?

A him

B he

C they

D his

10. Read sentence 7.

Levi ran full speed the to blocks to the bus stop and boarded the bus!

What is the correct way to write the underlined word?

A too

B two

C through

D Correct as is.

Name ______________________________ Date ______________

On your answer sheet, darken the circle for each correct answer.

11. What word completes this sentence?

Every day, they _______ Max at the park.

A seen

B sees

C seeing

D see

12. What word completes the sentence?

The baby will _______ in the high chair during breakfast.

A seat

B set

C sit

D sat

13. Which sentence is written correctly?

A Some elephants live time.

B A very long time is how elephants live.

C Some elephants live a very long time.

D Some elephants they live a very long time.

14. What word completes the sentence?

Which language is the _______ to learn: Chinese, Spanish, or Arabic?

A hardest

B harder

C hard

D most harder

15. What word completes the sentence?

_______ class walked quietly down the hall.

A Mr. Warren

B Mr. Warren's

C Mr. Warrens'

D Mr. Warrens

Name ______________________________ Date ______________

On your answer sheet, darken the circle for each correct answer.

16. What part of speech is the underlined word?

> Lance's mother gave <u>him</u> a catcher's mitt.

A noun

B pronoun

C verb

D adjective

17. Which verb completes this sentence?

> Dad ________ for Ladonna to go on the field trip.

A pay

B have paid

C payed

D paid

18. Which sentence is written most clearly?

A They skated on the frozen pond.

B On the frozen they skated the pond.

C Skated they on the frozen pond.

D On the frozen pond did they skate.

19. What word **best** completes the sentence?

> Her ________ garden is overflowing with beans.

A families

B familys'

C family's

D familys's

20. Which answer **best** combines these two sentences?

> Long ago people got cold.
> They sat around a fire.

A Long ago people got cold, they sat around a fire.

B Long ago people sat around a fire to get cold.

C Long ago people got cold, so they sat around a fire.

D Long ago people sat around a fire, so they got cold.

Name ______________________________ Date ______________

Read the passage. Then, answer the questions. On your answer sheet, darken the circle for each correct answer.

(1) Nicole and her family went to the World's Fair in paris, france. **(2)** They arrived at the fair on Saturday June 1, 1889. **(3)** The first thing they saw was the brand new Eiffel Tower. **(4)** It towered over all of the other buildings in the city. **(5)** Nicole's family spent all day at the fair. **(6)** After the fair, they went to the Louvre Museum and saw many beutiful works of art. **(7)** Before their trip was over, they walked to a famous church at the top of a hill. **(8)** They looked out over the buildings' rooves to the blue sky of the gorgeous city!

21. What is the correct way to write sentence 1?

A Nicole and her Family went to the World's Fair in Paris, France.

B Nicole and her family went to the World's Fair in Paris, France.

C Nicole and her family went to the world's fair in paris, france.

D Correct as is.

22. What is the correct way to write sentence 2?

A They arrived at the fair on Saturday June 1 1889.

B They arrived at the fair on, Saturday June 1, 1889.

C They arrived at the fair on Saturday, June 1, 1889.

D Correct as is.

Name ______________________________ Date ______________

23. What is the correct way to write sentence 3?

A The first thing they saw was the brand new eiffel tower.

B The first thing they saw was the Brand New Eiffel Tower.

C The first thing They saw was the brand new Eiffel tower.

D Correct as is.

24. What is the correct way to spell rooves in sentence 8?

A roofs

B roovies

C rofes

D Correct as is.

25. Which word in sentence 6 is misspelled?

A fair

B Museum

C beutiful

D art

Name ____________________ Date ____________

Read the passage. Then, answer the questions. On your answer sheet, darken the circle for each correct answer.

(1) We see Thomas Edison's inventions everywhere. **(2)** Do you know some of his inventions **(3)** Without him, you could never turn on a light. **(4)** Did you know that Edison invented the alectric lamp in 1879? **(5)** Films are shown on one of his inventions. **(6)** Music is listened to on one of his inventions. **(7)** He invented both the movie projector and the phonograph. **(8)** Many agree that Mister Edison is the greatest inventor who ever lived. **(9)** He even wrote the book the diary of Thomas A. Edison.

26. What punctuation mark is needed in sentence 2?

A .

B ,

C ?

D !

27. Read sentence 4.

Did you know that Edison invented the alectric lamp in 1879?

Which of the underlined words is spelled incorrectly?

A know

B invented

C alectric

D lamp

Name ______________________ Date ____________

28. What is the correct way to write sentence 6?

A Music is listened to, on one of his inventions.

B Music, is listened to on one of his inventions.

C Music is listened to on one, of his inventions.

D Correct as is.

29. Read sentence 8.

Many agree that Mister Edison is the greatest inventor who ever lived.

What is the correct way to write an abbreviation of the underlined word?

A Mr.

B Mr

C mr.

D mr

30. What is the correct way to write the title in sentence 9?

A The diary of Thomas a. Edison

B The Diary of Thomas A. Edison

C The diary of thomas a. edison

D Correct as is.

Name ________________________________ Date ________________

On your answer sheet, darken the circle for each correct answer.

31. Which sentence is correct?

A "Would you like to hear a silly joke? Tia asked."

B "Would you like to hear" a silly joke? Tia asked.

C "Would you like to hear a silly joke?" Tia asked.

D Would you like to hear a silly joke? Tia asked.

32. Which sentence contains errors?

A King Midas said, "I have the golden touch!"

B Without thinking, King Midas hugged his daughter.

C Quick as a wink she turned to gold?

D How does the book King Midas and the Golden Touch end?

33. What is the correct way to write this sentence?

I ride to school with three friends: Melita Yolanda and Orlando.

A I ride to school with three friends: Melita, Yolanda, and Orlando.

B I ride to school with three friends: Melita Yolanda and, Orlando.

C I ride to school with three friends: Melita. Yolanda, and, Orlando.

D Correct as is.

34. Which sentence uses the underlined word incorrectly?

A There are a lot of problems on this math test.

B The children got their books and went to school.

C They're going to the movies.

D The family of robins have left there nest.

Name ______________________________ Date ______________

On your answer sheet, darken the circle for each correct answer.

35. Which sentence has correct capitalization?

A Have you seen the movie Toy story?

B I read The Very Hungry Caterpillar to my nephew.

C Ezra Jack Keats wrote A letter to Amy.

D Is the book Babe the Gallant pig the same story as the movie babe?

36. Which sentence has a punctuation error?

A Uncle Robert lives in Springfield, Ohio.

B My sister is reading Harry Potter and the Chamber of Secrets.

C My little brother was born October 27 2011.

D An important date in history is July 20, 1969.

37. Which sentence is correct?

A Quinn "stood up and yelled, I need help!"

B Quinn stood up and "yelled, I need help!"

C Quinn stood up and yelled, "I need help!"

D Quinn stood "up and yelled, I need help!"

38. Choose the correctly spelled word to complete the sentence.

I found a ______ of socks in the dryer.

A par

B pare

C pear

D pair

39. Which sentence is correct?

A Jeri, and Matt, like to go to the beach

B Do you like to spend time at the beach?

C Watch out for the crabs?

D Did, Jeri step on a shell.

40. Which sentence has punctuation errors?

A Aiden said, "I don't like to use an escalator."

B "That's funny because elevators make me nervous!" Emma replied.

C "Lets take the stairs then, Aiden" suggested.

D Emma grabbed Aiden's hand and said, "I've got a better idea!"

Name ______________________ Date ______________

Vocabulary

Read the passage. Then, answer the questions. On your answer sheet, darken the circle for each correct answer.

African elephants live south of the Sahara desert in Africa. They are huge. They are some of the most powerful animals on Earth. For instance, they can tear a tree out of the ground with just their trunks! Sadly, they are in danger of disappearing forever because people hunt them. In 1979, about one and a half million elephants lived in Africa. Now, less than one-half of that number survives. Today, African elephants no longer roam over a wide area. Most live in small patches of forest and grassland and on government land.

41. Read these sentences.

> They are some of the most powerful animals on Earth. For instance, they can tear a tree out of the ground with just their trunks!

What does the word powerful mean?

A without power

B full of power

C having the most power

D giving power to others

42. Read this sentence.

> Today, African elephants no longer roam over a wide area.

What word means the **same as** roam?

A wander

B hunt

C run

D live

Name ______________________ Date ______________

Read the passage. Then, answer the questions. On your answer sheet, darken the circle for each correct answer.

Diary of a Cowboy

It looks like it's going to be another day of chasing those two horses! No one has been able to catch them all winter.

Ben and I headed out at dawn. We found the two horses down by the South Fork. They were as skittish as could be! Those horses took off before we got within a quarter mile of them.

We rode along patiently for a long way, hoping they'd get tired out. Then, Ben got ants in his pants. He took off after those horses at a hard gallop. I couldn't do anything but try to keep up. We chased them for 15 miles before they tired enough to let us get close and throw a rope on them.

We sure were two tired cowpokes by the time we brought those horses back to the ranch. Tomorrow should be an easier day. Ben and I will be fixing fences.

43. Read the sentences from the second paragraph.

> They were as skittish as could be! Those horses took off before we got within a quarter mile of them.

What does the word skittish mean?

A nervous

B strong

C dangerous

D silly

44. Read the sentences from the third paragraph.

> We rode along patiently for a long way, hoping they'd get tired out. Then, Ben got ants in his pants. He took off after those horses at a hard gallop.

What do the underlined words mean?

A Ben had to change his clothes.

B Ben thought he saw a nest of ants.

C Ben got an itch and had to walk.

D Ben got restless and impatient.

Name ______________________________ Date ______________

On your answer sheet, darken the circle for each correct answer.

45. Which definition of beat is used in the sentence below?

> **beat** (bēt)
> *noun*
> 1. a unit in music or poetry
> *noun*
> 2. the ticking sound made by a watch
> *verb*
> 3. to mix by stirring with a fork
> *verb*
> 4. to defeat in a game

> He beat the eggs while I made toast.

A Definition 1

B Definition 2

C Definition 3

D Definition 4

46. Which word does **not** belong in this group?

Monday	Wednesday
April	Friday

A Friday

B Monday

C April

D Wednesday

47. Which word has both underlined meanings?

> the center of a storm
> what we use to see with

A rain

B glass

C thunder

D eye

48. Which word **best** completes the sentence?

> The lifeguard blew her whistle and ________, "No horseplay in the pool!"

A whispered

B commented

C yelled

D mumbled

Name ______________________________ Date ______________

On your answer sheet, darken the circle for each correct answer.

49. Which word has the **opposite** meaning of the underlined word?

This is a special occasion.

A rare

B ordinary

C serious

D happy

50. Choose the word that **best** completes the sentence.

Memorial Day is a ______ holiday that is observed throughout our country.

A national

B local

C monthly

D colorful

51. Choose the word with a meaning that fits both sentences.

May I use this ______ to measure that picture frame? The citizens are pleased with the new ______ they elected.

A yardstick

B king

C ruler

D president

52. Read this sentence.

The preview made me want to come back to see the movie.

What does the word preview mean?

A a short showing after

B a short showing before

C a short showing during

D a short showing again and again

Writing Practice Test

Name ____________________ Date ____________

Writing Prompt 1

Plan and write an opinion in response to this writing prompt. Write your response on a separate sheet of paper. When you are done, proofread what you have written.

Do you think students should finish their homework before they can watch TV? Why or why not? Write an essay for your school newspaper that explains why you feel the way you do.

As you write your response, be sure to

- Write about only one topic.
- Include at least two reasons to support your opinion.
- Include specific details; use examples and reasons to support your ideas.
- Use a variety of complete sentences.
- Use logical organization with an introduction, body, and conclusion.

Name ______________________________ Date ______________

Writing Prompt 2

Plan and write a description in response to this writing prompt. Write your response on a separate sheet of paper. When you are done, proofread what you have written.

Think about a holiday you know well. Write a description of this holiday. Explain how and why it is celebrated.

As you write your response, be sure to

- Write about only one holiday.
- Include specific details.
- Explain *who*, *what*, *when*, *where*, *why*, and *how*.
- Use a variety of complete sentences.
- Use a logical organization with an obvious introduction, body, and conclusion.

Name ______________________________ Date ______________

Writing Prompt 3

Plan and write a story in response to this writing prompt. Write your response on a separate sheet of paper. When you are done, proofread what you have written.

Think about your favorite person from history. Write a story about spending a day with this person.

As you write your response, be sure to

- Describe your surroundings and the characters.
- Clearly tell a story that includes descriptive details. Include dialogue, if appropriate.
- Use a variety of complete sentences.
- Use logical organization with an obvious beginning, middle, and end.

Answer Sheets and Answer Key

Answer Sheets

Reading Practice: Literature

1 Ⓐ Ⓑ Ⓒ Ⓓ
2 Ⓐ Ⓑ Ⓒ Ⓓ
3 Ⓐ Ⓑ Ⓒ Ⓓ
4 Ⓐ Ⓑ Ⓒ Ⓓ
5 Ⓐ Ⓑ Ⓒ Ⓓ
6 Write answers on a separate sheet of paper.
7 Ⓐ Ⓑ Ⓒ Ⓓ
8 Ⓐ Ⓑ Ⓒ Ⓓ
9 Ⓐ Ⓑ Ⓒ Ⓓ
10 Ⓐ Ⓑ Ⓒ Ⓓ
11 Ⓐ Ⓑ Ⓒ Ⓓ
12 Ⓐ Ⓑ Ⓒ Ⓓ
13 Write answers on a separate sheet of paper.
14 Ⓐ Ⓑ Ⓒ Ⓓ
15 Ⓐ Ⓑ Ⓒ Ⓓ
16 Ⓐ Ⓑ Ⓒ Ⓓ
17 Ⓐ Ⓑ Ⓒ Ⓓ
18 Ⓐ Ⓑ Ⓒ Ⓓ
19 Ⓐ Ⓑ Ⓒ Ⓓ
20 Ⓐ Ⓑ Ⓒ Ⓓ
21 Write answers on a separate sheet of paper.
22 Ⓐ Ⓑ Ⓒ Ⓓ
23 Ⓐ Ⓑ Ⓒ Ⓓ
24 Ⓐ Ⓑ Ⓒ Ⓓ
25 Ⓐ Ⓑ Ⓒ Ⓓ
26 Write answers on a separate sheet of paper.

Reading Practice: Informational Text

1 Ⓐ Ⓑ Ⓒ Ⓓ
2 Ⓐ Ⓑ Ⓒ Ⓓ
3 Ⓐ Ⓑ Ⓒ Ⓓ
4 Ⓐ Ⓑ Ⓒ Ⓓ
5 Ⓐ Ⓑ Ⓒ Ⓓ
6 Write answers on a separate sheet of paper.
7 Write answers on a separate sheet of paper.
8 Ⓐ Ⓑ Ⓒ Ⓓ
9 Ⓐ Ⓑ Ⓒ Ⓓ
10 Ⓐ Ⓑ Ⓒ Ⓓ
11 Ⓐ Ⓑ Ⓒ Ⓓ
12 Ⓐ Ⓑ Ⓒ Ⓓ
13 Ⓐ Ⓑ Ⓒ Ⓓ
14 Write answers on a separate sheet of paper.
15 Ⓐ Ⓑ Ⓒ Ⓓ
16 Ⓐ Ⓑ Ⓒ Ⓓ
17 Ⓐ Ⓑ Ⓒ Ⓓ
18 Ⓐ Ⓑ Ⓒ Ⓓ
19 Ⓐ Ⓑ Ⓒ Ⓓ
20 Ⓐ Ⓑ Ⓒ Ⓓ
21 Write answers on a separate sheet of paper.
22 Ⓐ Ⓑ Ⓒ Ⓓ
23 Ⓐ Ⓑ Ⓒ Ⓓ
24 Ⓐ Ⓑ Ⓒ Ⓓ
25 Ⓐ Ⓑ Ⓒ Ⓓ
26 Ⓐ Ⓑ Ⓒ Ⓓ
27 Ⓐ Ⓑ Ⓒ Ⓓ
28 Write answers on a separate sheet of paper.

Language Arts Practice

1 Ⓐ Ⓑ Ⓒ Ⓓ	15 Ⓐ Ⓑ Ⓒ Ⓓ	29 Ⓐ Ⓑ Ⓒ Ⓓ
2 Ⓐ Ⓑ Ⓒ Ⓓ	16 Ⓐ Ⓑ Ⓒ Ⓓ	30 Ⓐ Ⓑ Ⓒ Ⓓ
3 Ⓐ Ⓑ Ⓒ Ⓓ	17 Ⓐ Ⓑ Ⓒ Ⓓ	31 Ⓐ Ⓑ Ⓒ Ⓓ
4 Ⓐ Ⓑ Ⓒ Ⓓ	18 Ⓐ Ⓑ Ⓒ Ⓓ	32 Ⓐ Ⓑ Ⓒ Ⓓ
5 Ⓐ Ⓑ Ⓒ Ⓓ	19 Ⓐ Ⓑ Ⓒ Ⓓ	33 Ⓐ Ⓑ Ⓒ Ⓓ
6 Ⓐ Ⓑ Ⓒ Ⓓ	20 Ⓐ Ⓑ Ⓒ Ⓓ	34 Ⓐ Ⓑ Ⓒ Ⓓ
7 Ⓐ Ⓑ Ⓒ Ⓓ	21 Ⓐ Ⓑ Ⓒ Ⓓ	35 Ⓐ Ⓑ Ⓒ Ⓓ
8 Ⓐ Ⓑ Ⓒ Ⓓ	22 Ⓐ Ⓑ Ⓒ Ⓓ	36 Ⓐ Ⓑ Ⓒ Ⓓ
9 Ⓐ Ⓑ Ⓒ Ⓓ	23 Ⓐ Ⓑ Ⓒ Ⓓ	37 Ⓐ Ⓑ Ⓒ Ⓓ
10 Ⓐ Ⓑ Ⓒ Ⓓ	24 Ⓐ Ⓑ Ⓒ Ⓓ	38 Ⓐ Ⓑ Ⓒ Ⓓ
11 Ⓐ Ⓑ Ⓒ Ⓓ	25 Ⓐ Ⓑ Ⓒ Ⓓ	39 Ⓐ Ⓑ Ⓒ Ⓓ
12 Ⓐ Ⓑ Ⓒ Ⓓ	26 Ⓐ Ⓑ Ⓒ Ⓓ	40 Ⓐ Ⓑ Ⓒ Ⓓ
13 Ⓐ Ⓑ Ⓒ Ⓓ	27 Ⓐ Ⓑ Ⓒ Ⓓ	
14 Ⓐ Ⓑ Ⓒ Ⓓ	28 Ⓐ Ⓑ Ⓒ Ⓓ	

Vocabulary Practice

1 Ⓐ Ⓑ Ⓒ Ⓓ	6 Ⓐ Ⓑ Ⓒ Ⓓ	11 Ⓐ Ⓑ Ⓒ Ⓓ
2 Ⓐ Ⓑ Ⓒ Ⓓ	7 Ⓐ Ⓑ Ⓒ Ⓓ	12 Ⓐ Ⓑ Ⓒ Ⓓ
3 Ⓐ Ⓑ Ⓒ Ⓓ	8 Ⓐ Ⓑ Ⓒ Ⓓ	13 Ⓐ Ⓑ Ⓒ Ⓓ
4 Ⓐ Ⓑ Ⓒ Ⓓ	9 Ⓐ Ⓑ Ⓒ Ⓓ	14 Ⓐ Ⓑ Ⓒ Ⓓ
5 Ⓐ Ⓑ Ⓒ Ⓓ	10 Ⓐ Ⓑ Ⓒ Ⓓ	15 Ⓐ Ⓑ Ⓒ Ⓓ

Writing Practice

Writing Prompt 1: Write response on your own paper.

Writing Prompt 2: Write response on your own paper.

Writing Prompt 3: Write response on your own paper.

Reading Practice Test

1 Ⓐ Ⓑ Ⓒ Ⓓ
2 Ⓐ Ⓑ Ⓒ Ⓓ
3 Ⓐ Ⓑ Ⓒ Ⓓ
4 Ⓐ Ⓑ Ⓒ Ⓓ
5 Ⓐ Ⓑ Ⓒ Ⓓ
6 Write answers on a separate sheet of paper.
7 Ⓐ Ⓑ Ⓒ Ⓓ
8 Ⓐ Ⓑ Ⓒ Ⓓ
9 Ⓐ Ⓑ Ⓒ Ⓓ
10 Ⓐ Ⓑ Ⓒ Ⓓ
11 Ⓐ Ⓑ Ⓒ Ⓓ
12 Ⓐ Ⓑ Ⓒ Ⓓ
13 Ⓐ Ⓑ Ⓒ Ⓓ
14 Write answers on a separate sheet of paper.
15 Ⓐ Ⓑ Ⓒ Ⓓ
16 Ⓐ Ⓑ Ⓒ Ⓓ
17 Ⓐ Ⓑ Ⓒ Ⓓ
18 Ⓐ Ⓑ Ⓒ Ⓓ
19 Ⓐ Ⓑ Ⓒ Ⓓ
20 Ⓐ Ⓑ Ⓒ Ⓓ
21 Write answers on a separate sheet of paper.
22 Ⓐ Ⓑ Ⓒ Ⓓ
23 Ⓐ Ⓑ Ⓒ Ⓓ
24 Ⓐ Ⓑ Ⓒ Ⓓ
25 Ⓐ Ⓑ Ⓒ Ⓓ
26 Ⓐ Ⓑ Ⓒ Ⓓ
27 Write answers on a separate sheet of paper.
28 Ⓐ Ⓑ Ⓒ Ⓓ
29 Ⓐ Ⓑ Ⓒ Ⓓ
30 Ⓐ Ⓑ Ⓒ Ⓓ
31 Ⓐ Ⓑ Ⓒ Ⓓ
32 Ⓐ Ⓑ Ⓒ Ⓓ
33 Write answers on a separate sheet of paper.
34 Ⓐ Ⓑ Ⓒ Ⓓ
35 Ⓐ Ⓑ Ⓒ Ⓓ
36 Ⓐ Ⓑ Ⓒ Ⓓ
37 Ⓐ Ⓑ Ⓒ Ⓓ
38 Ⓐ Ⓑ Ⓒ Ⓓ
39 Ⓐ Ⓑ Ⓒ Ⓓ
40 Write answers on a separate sheet of paper.
41 Ⓐ Ⓑ Ⓒ Ⓓ
42 Ⓐ Ⓑ Ⓒ Ⓓ
43 Ⓐ Ⓑ Ⓒ Ⓓ
44 Ⓐ Ⓑ Ⓒ Ⓓ
45 Ⓐ Ⓑ Ⓒ Ⓓ
46 Write answers on a separate sheet of paper.
47 Ⓐ Ⓑ Ⓒ Ⓓ
48 Ⓐ Ⓑ Ⓒ Ⓓ
49 Ⓐ Ⓑ Ⓒ Ⓓ
50 Ⓐ Ⓑ Ⓒ Ⓓ
51 Ⓐ Ⓑ Ⓒ Ⓓ
52 Ⓐ Ⓑ Ⓒ Ⓓ
53 Write answers on a separate sheet of paper.
54 Ⓐ Ⓑ Ⓒ Ⓓ
55 Ⓐ Ⓑ Ⓒ Ⓓ
56 Ⓐ Ⓑ Ⓒ Ⓓ
57 Ⓐ Ⓑ Ⓒ Ⓓ
58 Ⓐ Ⓑ Ⓒ Ⓓ
59 Ⓐ Ⓑ Ⓒ Ⓓ
60 Write answers on a separate sheet of paper.

Language Arts and Vocabulary Practice Test

1 Ⓐ Ⓑ Ⓒ Ⓓ	19 Ⓐ Ⓑ Ⓒ Ⓓ	37 Ⓐ Ⓑ Ⓒ Ⓓ
2 Ⓐ Ⓑ Ⓒ Ⓓ	20 Ⓐ Ⓑ Ⓒ Ⓓ	38 Ⓐ Ⓑ Ⓒ Ⓓ
3 Ⓐ Ⓑ Ⓒ Ⓓ	21 Ⓐ Ⓑ Ⓒ Ⓓ	39 Ⓐ Ⓑ Ⓒ Ⓓ
4 Ⓐ Ⓑ Ⓒ Ⓓ	22 Ⓐ Ⓑ Ⓒ Ⓓ	40 Ⓐ Ⓑ Ⓒ Ⓓ
5 Ⓐ Ⓑ Ⓒ Ⓓ	23 Ⓐ Ⓑ Ⓒ Ⓓ	41 Ⓐ Ⓑ Ⓒ Ⓓ
6 Ⓐ Ⓑ Ⓒ Ⓓ	24 Ⓐ Ⓑ Ⓒ Ⓓ	42 Ⓐ Ⓑ Ⓒ Ⓓ
7 Ⓐ Ⓑ Ⓒ Ⓓ	25 Ⓐ Ⓑ Ⓒ Ⓓ	43 Ⓐ Ⓑ Ⓒ Ⓓ
8 Ⓐ Ⓑ Ⓒ Ⓓ	26 Ⓐ Ⓑ Ⓒ Ⓓ	44 Ⓐ Ⓑ Ⓒ Ⓓ
9 Ⓐ Ⓑ Ⓒ Ⓓ	27 Ⓐ Ⓑ Ⓒ Ⓓ	45 Ⓐ Ⓑ Ⓒ Ⓓ
10 Ⓐ Ⓑ Ⓒ Ⓓ	28 Ⓐ Ⓑ Ⓒ Ⓓ	46 Ⓐ Ⓑ Ⓒ Ⓓ
11 Ⓐ Ⓑ Ⓒ Ⓓ	29 Ⓐ Ⓑ Ⓒ Ⓓ	47 Ⓐ Ⓑ Ⓒ Ⓓ
12 Ⓐ Ⓑ Ⓒ Ⓓ	30 Ⓐ Ⓑ Ⓒ Ⓓ	48 Ⓐ Ⓑ Ⓒ Ⓓ
13 Ⓐ Ⓑ Ⓒ Ⓓ	31 Ⓐ Ⓑ Ⓒ Ⓓ	49 Ⓐ Ⓑ Ⓒ Ⓓ
14 Ⓐ Ⓑ Ⓒ Ⓓ	32 Ⓐ Ⓑ Ⓒ Ⓓ	50 Ⓐ Ⓑ Ⓒ Ⓓ
15 Ⓐ Ⓑ Ⓒ Ⓓ	33 Ⓐ Ⓑ Ⓒ Ⓓ	51 Ⓐ Ⓑ Ⓒ Ⓓ
16 Ⓐ Ⓑ Ⓒ Ⓓ	34 Ⓐ Ⓑ Ⓒ Ⓓ	52 Ⓐ Ⓑ Ⓒ Ⓓ
17 Ⓐ Ⓑ Ⓒ Ⓓ	35 Ⓐ Ⓑ Ⓒ Ⓓ	
18 Ⓐ Ⓑ Ⓒ Ⓓ	36 Ⓐ Ⓑ Ⓒ Ⓓ	

Writing Practice Test

Writing Prompt 1: Write response on your own paper.

Writing Prompt 2: Write response on your own paper.

Writing Prompt 3: Write response on your own paper.